QUALITY CONTROL

QUALITY CONTROL
by Statistical Methods

G. HERDAN
D.I.C. M.Sc. (*Lond.*) Ph.D (*Vienna*)
LL.D. (*Prague*)

With 59 Diagrams 9 Tables and 5 Charts

THOMAS NELSON AND SONS LTD
LONDON EDINBURGH PARIS MELBOURNE
TORONTO AND NEW YORK

THOMAS NELSON AND SONS LTD
Parkside Works Edinburgh 9
3 Henrietta Street London WC2
312 Flinders Street Melbourne C1
91–93 Wellington Street West   Toronto 1

THOMAS NELSON AND SONS
385 Madison Avenue New York 17

SOCIÉTÉ FRANÇAISE D'EDITIONS NELSON
25 rue Henri Barbusse Paris Vᵉ

———————

First published 1948

PREFACE

QUALITY CONTROL is not a new statistical theory, but a most convenient arrangement of the geometry of statistical distributions. So convenient, in fact, that it enables the practical production man to handle that " perilous stuff " *probability* in a most efficient manner. He thus becomes the master of chance in its manifold influences upon the quality of manufactured product, instead of its victim.

This feature of being not a new theory but a convenient arrangement of the mathematics involved in statistical problems Quality Control has in common with a method which is both more difficult to handle and more ambitious in its aims, called Analysis of Variance, and which has become an important tool for ascertaining the source of variability of industrial product. The relation between the two methods, given by the fact that Analysis of Variance arranges the *arithmetic* of statistical problems in a way very similar to how Quality Control arranges their *geometry*, has been stressed throughout the relevant portions of this book, and this has been found to offer an easy approach to two methods otherwise not easily accessible to the general reader : Analysis of Variance and Theory of Correlation.

Concerning the representation of statistical methods, I have acted upon the principle that mathematics is a language —in symbols instead of in letters—which can be translated, like any other language, into English, and ought to be if the reader is to become familiar with " the Why and the Wherefore," and not only with the " How," of applying statistical methods. This book should therefore be looked upon not merely as a manual of mechanical rules for the application of statistical methods, but as one of statistical thought. If the reader learns to look at it in this way, he will find it helpful in many other ways of life.

There is, however, as any practical linguist knows, a limit to " translatability " from one language into another. Certain expressions in one language have no exact equivalent in the other.   Instead of making the translation too heavy and unwieldy by circumscribing such expressions, it is often better to use them as " loan words." The reader should regard in the same way the mathematical expressions—symbols and formulae—used in this book, whose amount, however, has been cut down to a minimum.   He should take them " on loan," and not omit to pay interest on them by a full understanding of their meaning.   If he has had secondary school education, he will find himself amply equipped for following the mathematical reasoning.   In fact, it does not presuppose a thing beyond the four fundamental arithmetical operations of adding, subtracting, multiplication, and division, and some understanding of graphs.

This book has grown out of lectures delivered before audiences of men and women engaged in production.   Since to the majority of them the term " Statistics " meant nothing but the (so it seemed to them) " dry and tedious " procedures for collecting information about Marriages, Births and Deaths for purposes of the Registrar-General, and since they were required to translate into practice almost immediately what they were taught at these lectures, it seemed imperative for obtaining good results to make the subject as palatable as could be.

To rouse their interest and make the matter take firm roots in their minds, their attention was drawn to what may be called the " Romance of Chance," in keeping with Prof. Whitehead's dictum when criticizing conventional scientific education: " Without the adventure of Romance you get inert knowledge and, at its worst, a contempt of ideas." This line of approach has been preserved in the design, execution and style of the book.

A good deal of the difficulties and doubts of the audience as they came up during the discussions, and on subsequent occasions during shop inspection, has been worked into the text.   The book has thus become a sort of translation of production and inspection problems into the language of statistics, rather than a collection of examples to illustrate the theorems of statistics.

The book is meant to form an introduction to *all* branches

of Quality Control which have been found useful in practical work, such as the principal technique of *Control Charts* (Chapters II and VI), first developed by Shewhart, Pearson, Dudding, and Jennett, the technique of *Probability Graphs* (Chapters III and 7.8–7.11), two standard methods of *Sampling Inspection* (Chapters VII and VIII), due to L. E. Simon and Dodge-Romig, and two methods indispensable for judging experimental results, *Analysis of Variance* (Chapter IV) and *Correlations* (Chapter V).*

Apart from the references given above and the works cited in their appropriate places, indebtedness is expressed to authors and publishers for permission to reprint tables and diagrams from the following works :

Davies and Pearson, " Methods of Estimating from Samples the Population Standard Deviation," *J.R.S.S.*, vol. i, No. 1, 1934.

Croxton and Crowder, *Applied General Statistics*. London, Pitman & Sons, Ltd.

L. E. Simon, *An Engineer's Manual of Statistical Methods*. New York, John Wiley & Sons ; London, Chapman & Hall.

Dodge and Romig, " Single Sampling and Double Sampling Inspection Tables," *The Bell System Technical Journal*, published by the American Telephone and Telegraph Company, 195 Broadway, New York.

In a work of this kind it is neither possible nor necessary to give exact references for the authorship of each detail of theory or procedure. Consequently, I have not thought it necessary to stress my own authorship in places where a method or some information of theoretical interest was due to myself. The reader acquainted with the literature of Quality Control will no doubt find several new departures in theory and method, but it is before all the welding of the various branches of Quality Control into one unified whole, attempted here for the first time, which is claimed as original.

As far as examples are taken from actual experience, they have been altered so as to avoid disclosing actual processes but not in a way prejudicial to their illustrative value.

---

* Since this was written, *Statistical Quality Control* by E. L. Grant has been published in U.S.A.

CONTENTS

APPENDICES I to XII

NOTE

Numeration of Paragraphs, Figures, and Equations

Each paragraph in this book is distinguished by a number consisting of the chapter number prefixed to the number of the paragraph in the chapter, e.g. 5.9 means the ninth paragraph of Chapter V. A similar system of numeration is used for tables, figures, and equations, e.g. Fig. 3.2 means the second figure in Chapter III, and similarly for tables and equations.

CHAPTER I

LAWS OF CHANCE—THE NORMAL LAW OF ERRORS

1.1 The Case Against 100 per cent. Inspection

IN industrial work we are always faced with the problem of having to judge lot quality from sample quality.

There seems to be one royal road for judging lot quality, and that is by testing everything. This is called 100 per cent. inspection. Close examination shows that 100 per cent. inspection is not infallible.

The reasons against it are these :

(1) 100 per cent. inspection is seldom done, even when it is supposed to be done. The examiner in charge of it will usually test as much as he or she can, and then pass on the rest unexamined.

(2) Even when 100 per cent. inspection is conscientiously done one cannot expect it to be without errors. If an examiner is required to test, say, 8,000 small articles for a certain dimension during one shift, it is inevitable that, sooner or later, errors will be committed. Inspection fatigue sets in very soon, as experience shows, and makes the inspection results more or less unreliable.

(3) Costs and labour required for 100 per cent. inspection are as a rule prohibitive. The use of gauging machines in place of human beings—where the characteristic is measurable—is no satisfactory way out of the difficulty, because it has been shown that gauging machines are subject to the same types of error as other processes in nature.

The alternative method for assessing lot quality is to take comparatively small samples and judge the quality of the lot from the quality of the samples.

Before the application of statistical laws to this kind of problem, the lot quality was simply taken to be the same as the sample quality. In other words, one did not take into account the fact that the sample was only a sample from the whole lot, and as such could show not only the same quality as the lot but also a better or worse quality.

One always had, of course, a vague idea that chance came into play whenever lot quality was judged in this way, but chance was considered to be of such an elusive character that the only thing that could be done about it was to ignore it. This was a very unsatisfactory state of affairs because one thus became the victim of chance instead of its master, and in most cases evidently judged lot quality wrongly.

1.2 Laws of Chance

There is, however, no longer any necessity for ignoring chance, because to-day a good deal is known about its working. In fact, *laws* of chance have been discovered from which it can be clearly seen that chance is not at all the mysterious entity which is supposed to suffer events to happen without a sufficient cause, but something much more prosaic. We have learned to tune chance a good deal flatter than we did before.

It is interesting to learn how people came to study chance. It was in the eighteenth century when the French aristocrats were desirous of making fortunes at the card table, or in other forms of gambling. In order to make sure of success they hired mathematicians to work out the perfect schemes for winning at these games of chance. Although it is not known whether they were rewarded in their efforts, the findings of the mathematicians are recorded, and represent the first books on the laws of chance. Later on those studies extended from games of chance to almost every branch of human knowledge and it was found that what these mathematicians had discovered were laws of nature, or, at least, mathematical laws.

1.3 The Normal Law of Errors

Quality Control is based upon certain laws of chance, and we shall therefore consider in detail what is meant by a Law of Chance.

Supposing a great number of shots are fired at a target by a fairly good marksman. Let the experiment be repeated a number of times, and let the experiment be repeated also by using different marksmen ; then the scatter of shots on the target will always be different from one experiment to the next, but in spite of these differences a certain pattern will be discernible. The pattern will be that the shots nearest the centre of the target will be most frequent, and their density will decrease as we move away from the centre in any direction.

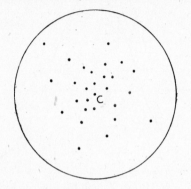

FIG. 1.1   Distribution of Shots on a Target

Let us further suppose that the target is divided into equal strips 1 in. wide. We can then " group " the observations on the target by counting the hits contained in one strip and erecting over a horizontal base representing our scale, rectangles, one for each strip interval, whose areas are proportionate to the number of observations in each strip.

The resulting picture is called a *histogram* (Fig. 1.2). If the total number of observations is increased indefinitely, so that the class intervals can be correspondingly decreased, and if the mid-points of the small side of the rectangles are connected by means of a continuous curve we arrive at what is called the Curve of Errors, or the Normal Law.

The algebraic expression of the normal curve is

$$y = \frac{h}{\sqrt{\pi}} e^{-h^2 x^2} = \frac{1}{\sigma\sqrt{2\pi}} e - \frac{1}{2}\left(\frac{x}{\sigma}\right)^2 ,$$

where x is the deviation of a measurement from the mean,
h is the measure of precision equalling $\dfrac{1}{\sigma\sqrt{2}}$,

σ is the standard deviation (see paragraph 2.1).

The integration of this expression between certain limits then gives the proportion P of measurements lying within these limits, and is known as the Error Function $P/2 = \dfrac{1}{\sigma\sqrt{2\pi}}\displaystyle\int^{x/\sigma} e - \dfrac{1}{2}\left(\dfrac{x}{\sigma}\right)^2 . dx$

(see Appendix I)

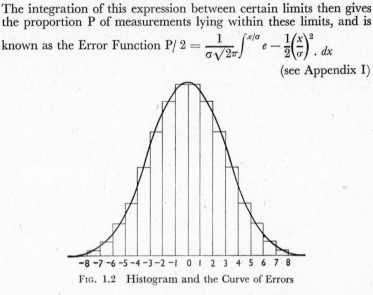

Fig. 1.2   Histogram and the Curve of Errors

This is the basic law of chance used in Quality Control work.

It is a law of *chance* for this reason. If somebody were to ask the marksmen what made their shots deviate from the point at which they precisely aimed, they would probably answer—barring any stronger language—" It is just chance." For the single shot there is no prediction possible as to where it will strike. One understands here, in a vague way, what the meaning of chance is. It is the combined effect of a multiplicity of very small causes, so small and so many that it is impossible to disentangle them or enumerate them, and consequently to predict the effect they will have on the aiming. In the present case, these small causes can be slight differences in powder, or in the dimension of the projectile, differences in the atmosphere, differences in position of the marksmen, etc.

It is a *law* of chance because, knowing the properties of the Curve of Error, it is possible to predict how many shots would, on pure chance, be observed within or without a certain distance on either side of the centre.

Let it be noted that it is not the shape of the curve which

matters but its structural properties. The shape of the curve may vary, but its fundamental properties remain the same. The most outstanding of these properties, which enables one to use the curve for prediction of the kind mentioned above, is this. If we project the point in the curve where the convex changes into the concave on to the base, the distance of that point from the mean is called *standard deviation*. Now the properties of the curve are such that no matter what its shape is like, there will always be the same proportion of observations within (or without) the same multiple of the standard deviation on either side of the mean. This makes prediction possible, and prediction is scientifically conceivable only if the matter is governed by a law.*

It is this Normal Law which, as observed, forms the basic concept of Quality Control. It is easy to see why this should be so. It has been found to apply everywhere in nature where a multiplicity of small causes brings about a certain effect. In industrial work it is this multiplicity of small causes which makes it difficult to work to what is called Specifications, laid down for important characteristics, which must be observed if the product is to be acceptable. If we think, for instance, of a certain characteristic like the length of an article, then the number of small causes entering into the process and determining the length dimension are legion. Consequently, the concept of chance will enter into our considerations. Now it has been found empirically that industrial measurements of that kind obey the normal law very nearly. That is, if the measurements of, say, length of an article, are taken for a considerable number of such articles, and are grouped in the way described above, the distribution will follow more or less closely the normal law. We are then able to predict how much of the bulk of the product will be within certain distances of the mean. We are also able to determine whether the bulk range is compatible with the specifications, and if not, to ascertain the causes that disturb a stable and, from the point of view of design and specification, acceptable production.

* For a clear and concise account of the mathematical ideas underlying the conception of the Normal Law, the reader is referred to Levy and Preidel, *Elementary Statistics* (Nelson)

1.4 Application of the Normal Law to Gunnery Work

Quality Control is essentially a method designed to assist the production people in their work. As such it is a simplification of statistical methods which it would otherwise be very difficult to apply to mass production.

To ascertain whether or not a distribution follows the Normal or any other law, and what is the particular shape of such a distribution is a difficult business, and people engaged in the production shops cannot be supposed to carry out calculations of that kind. A simplification is therefore necessary if statistical methods are to be of any use in practical work.

The necessity of transforming the complicated laws of chance into mathematical tools which are easy to handle has been felt in other branches of human knowledge, for instance, in gunnery work.

The gunnery officer in the field has no time to carry out a complicated analysis of the scatter of his shots. On the other hand, with our modern weapons it is necessary to do an analysis of a certain kind in order to know whether the gun is satisfactorily aimed.

If the gun is aimed at a certain distant point and a great number of shots are fired without altering the position of the gun, it has been found that the shots do not by any means all strike at one point. A scatter results, and the distribution of the shots in the main direction, say, of the scatter, follows the normal law. The reason is simply that a great number of small causes combine in bringing about deviations of the single shots from the centre of the distribution.

The distribution is briefly this : most of the shots will be around what is called the " centre of impact," which may or may not be on the target, and as one moves farther away from the centre of impact on either side, the number of shots per interval will decrease.

Taking an ideal case we would get the following distribution, where E represents a distance related to the above-mentioned standard deviation (in fact it is ·6745 times the standard deviation), called the Probable Error.

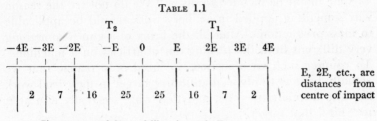

TABLE 1.1

Percentages of Shots falling in each Zone

Now supposing the gun in actual practice or in warfare is aimed at a certain distant object and a great number of shots are fired. The officer in charge of the gun wants to know whether the gun is correctly aimed and whether most of the shots really strike in effective distance of the target. He does not see where the shots strike but his observer officer reports the number of shots which are seen to strike beyond the target. Supposing he reports that 9 per cent. of the shots are seen to strike beyond the target (T_1). If the centre of impact was on the target, then 50 per cent. should be seen striking beyond and 50 per cent. short of the target. From the report received the gunnery officer knows immediately that the centre of impact has to be shifted by two probable errors in order to bring it on the target. The probable error for a type of gun, and also for the individual gun, is a known quantity, and the gun can be re-aimed accordingly.

To take another example, supposing the observer officer had reported that 25 per cent of the shots were seen to strike short of the target (T_2). Then the gunnery officer knows that the centre of impact has to be shifted backwards by one probable error in order to bring it on the target.

1.5 The Transition from " Probability of Fire " to " Probability of Good Production "

The same type of simplification for working with the normal law is also used in Quality Control work. Instead of constructing curves and ascertaining their properties, we work with certain distances from the mean, be it the specification mean or a calculated one, and ascertain the number of observations within and without these distances.

One might be inclined to say : " We do not see the reason why something applied in artillery work should be applicable to mass production. After all the firing of a gun is something very different from the turning out of articles on a machine." To counter such an objection, we need only realize that we actually have not only a quantitative target in industrial work but also a qualitative one, and that what we really aim at is to " hit " that target.

The qualitative target for industrial work is the Specification Mean, together with the Tolerances on either side of the mean. The product is acceptable only if the characteristic in question comes out within this target. It is thus actually, in the full sense of the term, a question of hitting the target. Furthermore, as has been pointed out under 1.3, the great number of small causes responsible for a given characteristic of an industrial article behave like any other combination of small causes : they produce a scatter or variation of measurements of that characteristic which more or less complies with the Law of Error. Seeing that in this respect the " Probability of Fire," as the gunnery officer calls it, and the " Probability of Good Work " in mass production are governed by the same type of law, we must conclude that the production man is simply in the position of the gunner, and the production engineer in the position of the gunnery officer, and that the machines or processes have to be directed by the help of Laws of Chance in such a way as to make the product come out on the target. Thus it is quite natural to apply to the control of mass production a simplification which has been found very useful in external ballistics. If for instance, we find that the average of the dimension in question would be a good distance from the Specification Mean, we know that the " centre of impact " of the process has to be shifted so as to bring it back to the specification mean. Or, if we were to find that the scatter is so great as to make the number of articles around the specification mean small, the Production Engineer has to do everything in his power to reduce that scatter so as to make the product come out properly within the target, thinning out towards its boundaries.

The statement that " industrial measurements . . . obey the normal law very nearly " (paragraph 1.3) is open to criticism if taken too literally. It is, in fact, an over-simplification in two respects.

Firstly, when we say that measurements are distributed according to a law of chance, this must not be taken to imply that there will be no assignable causes responsible, in varying degree, for some or all of the measurements of that kind. On the contrary, we must be fully alive to the fact that more often than not such disturbing causes will be present. It is just because of this that we need quality control to weed out these undesirable influences. It follows that a pure chance system will be the result rather than the starting-point of quality control work. The chance cause system which is, by definition, free from interference by assignable causes is thus not " given," as a rule, but is what we are aiming at. It is now an empirical fact that such a state *can* be reached by a suitable method of quality control.

Secondly, the form of the distribution of measurements is, as a rule, only approximately normal, and not infrequently distinctly skew. However, as we shall see in Chapter II, it is not the distribution of individual measurements with which we are directly concerned in Quality Control work, but that of the averages or other statistical parameters (characteristic quantities). Now it is again an empirical fact, supported and explained by statistical theory, that the distribution of averages (which is the most important statistic in this connection) is approximately normal even though that of the individual observations be very skew.

1.6 The Place of Quality Control in the Development of Statistical Method

What we call " statistical method " had its origin in the Theory of Errors. That theory taught us how to find the best approximation to the " true " value of a given thing, e.g. a physical constant, an atomic weight, the position of a star, etc. Only *one* value could here be the true value, and as the determinations were found to be always more or less discordant, among themselves, the arithmetic mean was taken as representing the best estimate of the " true " value, in accordance with the Theory of Errors.

Population statistics and biological statistics as we know them started when it was found empirically that the varying values of a given characteristic, such as the chest measurements of a certain male population between, say, 20 and 50 years of age, or the weight of a certain kind of beans, were distributed around a mean value similar to the measurements of a single thing.

But notwithstanding the formal likeness of distribution, the object is here a very different one. We have not any longer *one* thing which we measure repeatedly in order to ascertain its true value, but *different* individuals (representing probably as many " true " values) each of which is measured only once, and what we are after is not a " true " but the " typical " (mean) value of the characteristic for the given group of individuals, and its variability.

No doubt, if we measured an individual repeatedly, we would get somewhat discordant values. But the differences arising from such repeated measuring of one and the same individual are so small compared with the differences between different individuals that they can be neglected, and even *must* be neglected if we are to arrive at the kind of statistical information we are after in population and biological statistics.

The application of statistical method to industrial measurements represents the next logical step in the development of such methods. The speed with which manufacturing conditions change compels us to use what may be called " dynamic statistics."

Instead of assuming that we are dealing with *one* chance universe * whose statistical structure we determine so as to make comparisons possible with related chance universes, we now at the outset suspect that disturbing causes are present, or we take into account the possibility, if not probability, that the product represents a mixture of *different* chance universes.

Consequently, we are now primarily interested in the differences, or the distribution, of those values which are " typical " for each of the partial universes, which we suspect to have contributed to our total of observations, or of which we suspect that total to be compounded. To get the overall

* This is the term used for the total of observations

picture we want, and in order not to miss the forest because of the trees, we must now to some extent neglect the variation between individuals.

The distributions with which we are, therefore, concerned here are distributions of means and standard deviations or ranges. They are called the "Sampling Distributions" in contradistinction to the Frequency or Parent Distributions of the Individuals.

Chapter II

THE RAIL LINES OF CHANCE—QUALITY CONTROL CHARTS

2.1 Statistical Control of Quality

REMEMBERING what has been said above (1.3) about industrial measurements following closely the Normal Law, let us now see in detail what simplification has been devised for working with this law in industrial practice. We know already that the simplification is of exactly the same type as that used in Ballistics. The fundamental property of the Normal Curve is used according to which certain distances from the mean are invariably bound up with certain percentages of the area under the curve. If we project the point of the curve where the concave changes into the convex on to the x-axis, then the distance from the mean to this point is called the Standard Deviation, because it represents a specially important deviation. It is, in fact, so important that it is used as a general measure of dispersion. It divides the area under the curve in the ratio 2 : 1 (inside : outside). Realizing that the total area represents the total number of our observations (see Histogram, Fig. 1.2) we define the standard deviation as the distance from the mean for which there is a chance of 2 : 1 that an article picked out at random will not exceed it (see Fig. 2.1).

A similar regularity governs the chances of deviations at certain multiples of the standard deviation. At twice the standard deviation on both sides of the mean, the ratio of articles "within" (i.e. having deviations equal or smaller than two standard deviations) to those "without" (with dimensions greater than two standard deviations) is very nearly 19 : 1. This means that of 20 articles picked at random from a very great number of pieces, 19 would lie within twice the distance of the standard deviation on either side of the mean. We can also express it by saying that if we pick out one article, the chances that it will lie within that distance of twice the standard deviation on either side of the mean, to that of its having a dimension exceeding these limits are 19 : 1. At three times the standard deviation the ratio of articles "within" (i.e. having deviations equal or smaller than three times the standard deviation) to those "without" (i.e. with dimensions greater than three times the standard deviation) is 369 : 1.

This means that practically all the product will lie between plus and minus three times the standard deviation, provided that the variations of the characteristic measured are due only to chance, with no major causes interfering.

The following diagram represents the relationship between distance and frequency in a normal curve, in graphical form.*

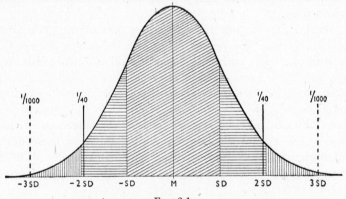

FIG. 2.1

The Normal Curve. Relationship between Deviation
and Frequency of Occurrence
SD represents the standard deviation
Area within ± SD to area outside as 2 : 1
Area within ± 2SD to area outside as 19 : 1
Area within ± 3SD is area outside as 369 : 1

2.2 The 1/40 and 1/1000 Control Limits

For practical work a further simplification has been introduced. Areas are imagined to be cut off at 1.96 and 3.09 standard deviations respectively. The advantage of doing so is that the chances of finding an article "within" these dimensions to those of finding it "without" are now exactly 19 : 1 and 500 : 1 respectively. The probability of a measurement lying beyond these limits on either side of the mean is now

* see Appendix I for the relationship in arithmetical form

exactly ·05 (5 per cent.) and ·002 (·2 per cent. or 2 in 1,000),
whereas at two and three standard deviations the probabilities
are ·046 and ·0027 respectively.

In the diagram 2.1, an area is cut off on either side of the
mean representing 2·5 per cent. on each side, or 5 per cent.
on both sides. As the total area under the curve represents
the total number of observations, there will be a chance of
5 in 100 or 1 in 20 or 2 in 40 that an observation will fall
outside that distance from the mean. As there is an equal
chance of a point falling outside on either side of the mean,
we call these lines 1 in 40 limits, meaning that there is a chance
of 1 in 40 observations that a point will fall outside one of the
control lines.

We further cut off the very small part of the area under
the curve which lies beyond 3·09 × S.D., which means that
an area of ·1 per cent. has been cut off on either side, and
therefore ·2 per cent. on both sides together.

Applying the reasoning as in the preceding paragraph, we
should expect two observations in 1,000 to fall outside both
these limits, or one observation in 1,000 outside each of these
limits. These lines are therefore called the 1 in 1,000 limits,
and represent the distances within which practically all of the
product is expected to lie.

2.3 How to Arrive at the Control Chart from the Diagram of the Normal Curve

From this diagram we easily arrive at the quality control
chart. All we have to do is to rotate it through a right angle
and, using the horizontal axis as the time scale, scatter the
observations of each interval in a horizontal direction according
to the time at which each observation was made. We then
obtain the diagram shown at the top of page 15.

The perpendicular lines erected at the specified distances,
1·96 and 3·09 standard deviations, from the mean have now
become two pairs of quality control lines, called the inner and
the outer limits. Provided that the process is controlled by
chance and the variations therefore due to nothing else but the
influence of chance, with no assignable causes disturbing the
chance variation, we should expect the frequency of observa-

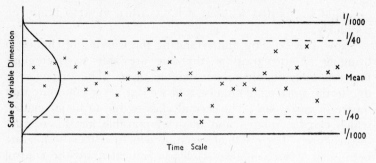

FIG. 2.2

Relation between Normal Curve and Quality Control Chart

tions within a certain range of values to comply with the percentages represented by these lines. That is, we should expect approximately 1 in 40 samples to fall outside one of the inner lines and practically nothing to fall beyond the outer lines.

2.4 Control Limits as the Boundaries Between Stability and Disturbance

What is achieved by having control lines of this sort is that we have now a kind of gauge for judging regularity or consistency of performance.

If the normal law, or any other law of chance, is adequate for the description of a certain frequency distribution, this means that the sole causes responsible for the scatter are chance causes. Furthermore, as such a complex of causes tends to be invariant, that is, to remain what it is, we are satisfied that the scatter produced by such a set of unavoidable causes will not change as long as no assignable cause interferes, and we may therefore regard the process as stable under the given set of conditions.

It goes without saying that it is essential in mass production for us to be able to assess the quality of the product in a reliable way. We should be able to depend on the quality varying no more than is unavoidable. It would not do to have the product one day conforming to a certain level and the next day conforming to another level. In other words, we want to be reasonably sure that the emergence of an assignable cause of variation—that is, a cause disturbing the working of chance

—should be spotted without delay, with a view to removing it quickly.

Now, it is only by understanding the working of chance in bringing about variations that we are able to distinguish between unavoidable and avoidable ones. The first class is due to the working of chance, and we can never eliminate that source of variation. The second class is due to major causes, which can be isolated and made responsible for this or that disturbance. The range of variation which we have to tolerate because it is unavoidable is clearly indicated by the control lines. It can be maintained that, without having an idea of how far the influence of chance is felt in a certain process, we could never distinguish between what is an avoidable and an unavoidable variation.

2.5 The Necessity for Economic Control of Quality as Distinct from Statistical Control

The part of the control system which has been explained up to now is that of statistical control. It goes without saying, however, that a process may be under good statistical control without meeting the requirements of the management for a particular kind of process. It might go on steadily from day to day within practically the same control limits, indicating stability of production, but these limits might not be in conformity with the specifications and the drawing tolerances.

This points to the necessity for completing the statistical control by what may be called economic control. It is not enough to watch the regularity of performance from day to day ; the product must also meet the specifications, otherwise it may be of little use to the management. That it is not enough to consider only whether all the product is within the control lines, will become clear from what follows.

We shall also see that our picture of the quality control chart has to be modified somewhat if it is to be of real use in practical work.

2.6 Control Lines for Averages (The Principle Explained)

One might conceivably reason like this : since the tolerances define the admissible range of bulk quality, they should be made to serve as 1/1000 control limits. The matter is, however, not quite so simple.

The reasons for not regarding the tolerances as control limits are :

(1) Such tolerances are not always compatible with the inherent variability of the process (see paragraph 2.4) ;

(2) the distribution of individuals, to which the tolerances refer, is less normal, and therefore less controllable than that of averages ;

(3) the established practice in Shop Inspection is to test by averages rather than by individual samples.

In industrial work it is not only the dimensions of individual articles which are recorded—and it is individual articles to which the control lines of Fig. 2.2 refer. The inspection procedure usually consists in taking a sample of a number of articles and calculating the average. The obvious idea is to cover a greater part of the process, and also to reduce the freak variations which may occur in one or another article.

Let us be a little more explicit about this. In industrial mass production we inspect for quality by taking not samples of 1 but of 5 to 10 if we measure, and of 20 to 50 if we gauge. The reason is obvious. If the rate of production is high— several thousand articles per hour, say—it is evident that a sample of 1 will not give an adequate picture of the quality of a batch of, say, 200 if taken every 10 minutes or so. We may hit upon an accidentally bad article which is in no way representative of the whole batch. If we asked for machine adjustment on the strength of that sample of 1, it would simply mean asking for trouble, and we would get it.

Conversely, one satisfactory article might occur in a run of bad work, and should therefore not be taken as an indication that the batch from which it came was all right.

Working with averages instead of with individual observations tends to give a better foundation for either asking or not asking for machine adjustment. Taking samples of 10, say, it is clear that the contribution due to the accidentally bad article would in the average be swamped by the contributions due to the 9 others. Conversely, the contribution of an accidentally good article would be swamped by the contributions of the remaining 9 bad articles.

But now an important question arises : We know how much deviation from the specification mean to tolerate in the individual observation. The tolerance on either side of the mean tells us that. But how much are we to allow for the deviations in the average from the specification mean and yet be satisfied that the bulk of the product will come within the tolerances ? What is wanted is evidently control lines for averages.

Now it is fortunate that long before anybody thought of applying statistical methods to industrial control, mathematicians had been successful in finding out by how much the averages of comparatively small samples picked at random from a great bulk of observations (called the " population ") are likely to vary among themselves, and also from the bulk mean or " true " mean. The information thus made available about the variation of averages, which was called the Sampling Distribution to distinguish it from the Frequency Distribution of individuals, came as a godsend when the above problem arose in mass production, viz. how far shall averages be allowed to vary if the product is still to be considered satisfactory ?

Before we give a more detailed account of these matters, we can show in a graphical way that specification tolerances are not suitable for controlling averages.

Let us assume that, as shown in Fig. 2.3 (page 19), averages are plotted on a chart having the specification tolerances as control lines, and that the averages come right up to the upper limit. As each point represents an average of, say, 5, the individual observations will be distributed around it, as indicated by the small circles. This shows clearly that individual observations may fall outside the specification, although the average lies within.

As the bulk of the product consists of individual observations it follows that in order to safeguard against part of the product being outside the specifications, we want limit lines well within the specification limits. How much they should lie within, in order to fulfil that function, will be shown in the following paragraphs.

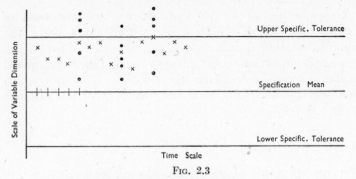

Fig. 2.3

Specification Tolerances and Sample Averages
Crosses denote sample averages
Dots denote individual measurements

2.7 The Relation Between the Distribution of Individuals and that of Averages (Quantitatively Explained)

Let us assume that for a certain measurable characteristic of a certain type of article, the specification value is given with a tolerance on either side. Let us call the specification value m and the tolerances t_u and t_l, and let these latter distances be placed symmetrically around the mean. Utilizing the information derived from experience, and used so widely in quality control, viz. that industrial measurements are, on the whole, distributed normally or very nearly so, we can assume that if the product was to meet the specifications it should be normally distributed around the specification mean with the tails of the distribution approaching the horizontal just at the distance of the upper and lower tolerances. In diagrammatic form it would appear thus :

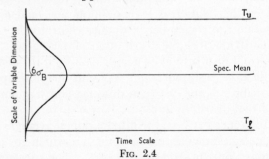

Fig. 2.4
Statistical Picture of the Bulk according to Specifications

Remembering what was said above about the bulk of normally distributed articles lying within three times the standard deviation approximately, on either side of the Mean, our assumption becomes equivalent to saying that the standard deviation (commonly written σ) in a bulk of articles which meets specifications fully, is approximately $\frac{1}{6}$ of the distance $t_u - t_l$. In symbols

$$\sigma_B = \frac{t_u - t_l}{6} \quad . \quad . \quad . \quad . \quad (2.1)$$

$1{\cdot}96\sigma_B$ on either side of the Mean (M) will then give the 1/40 limit, and $3{\cdot}09\sigma_B$ the 1/1000 limit for the individual articles in the bulk.

As has been observed above, in industrial inspection we work as a rule with averages. That is, we measure a number of articles, calculate the average, plot the averages obtained in regular intervals on a chart, and watch their distribution. The fundamental rule is that the averages should fall within the control lines in the assigned proportions. Practically no point should fall outside the 1 in 1,000 limit.

If, however, we want to use the control limits for controlling the distribution of averages, the diagram given above (Fig. 2.4) has to be modified. This diagram represents control limits for individual observations only—that is, for the observations forming the bulk of a product. What is wanted is control limits for averages. As we have already seen, in paragraph 2.6, the distribution of averages differs somewhat from that of the individuals. We now want the general rule for transforming the control lines for individuals into those for averages. Fortunately, the relation is a very simple one, and one of the most important to remember in quality control work.

As regards the form of distribution of averages, it happens to be a normal distribution or nearly so, even if the distribution of the bulk is far from normal. We can therefore apply with confidence the relation between distance and frequency given for the normal distribution by the Law of Errors.

The difference between the distribution of averages and that of individuals lies, therefore, not in the law which governs these distributions, but in something else. The distribution of averages is closer packed around the mean, representing a curve like the narrow curve in Fig. 2.5, and its standard deviation is reduced compared with that of the distribution of individuals in the ratio $1/\sqrt{n}$, where n is the sample size.

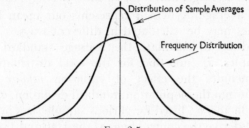

FIG. 2.5
Frequency Distribution and Distribution of Averages

The quantity $\dfrac{\sigma}{\sqrt{n}}$ is called the Standard Error of the Mean. Considering that it is nothing else but the standard deviation of the frequency distribution of averages or means, it is clear that two times that standard deviation or $\dfrac{2\sigma}{\sqrt{n}}$, and three times that standard deviation or $\dfrac{3\sigma}{\sqrt{n}}$, will represent approximately the distance from the mean of the $1/40$ and $1/1000$ limits respectively, for sample averages.

It follows that if we write for the standard deviation of averages of samples of n coming from a bulk which conforms fully with the specifications, the expression (from 2.1)

$$\sigma_A = \frac{\sigma_B}{\sqrt{n}} = \frac{t_u - t_l}{6\sqrt{n}} \quad . \quad . \quad . \quad . \quad (2.2)$$

then $1 \cdot 96\sigma_A$ will give the $1/40$ and $3/09\sigma_A$ the $1/000$ limit for averages to be placed symmetrically on both sides of the specification mean.

2.8 How Control Limits are Obtained from Actual Samples

Up to now we have been only concerned with the specification bulk, that is, with control lines for 100 per cent. perfect product. We must now turn our attention to the *actual* quality

of the product which is to be ascertained from periodically taken
samples.

Let us assume that actual samples were taken over a considerable period of time. For each of the samples we then
calculate the average, and from all these averages what is called
the grand average $\overline{X}$, which represents our mean line. The
control lines may be calculated in different ways. The direct
way would be to calculate the average standard deviation
within samples, $\overline{s}_n$ (not that for the total distribution which
possibly includes the effect of variation *between* samples),
transform it into the population standard deviation, σ, by dividing it by a factor, b_n, listed for various sample sizes in Appendix
III (*a*) and derive the control lines as the 1/40 and 1/1000 limits
for averages, using the expressions $\dfrac{1 \cdot 96\sigma}{\sqrt{n}}$ and $\dfrac{3 \cdot 09\sigma}{\sqrt{n}}$ respectively.* The simplest way, however, is to obtain them from
the range. The range is the difference between the greatest
and smallest dimensions in one sample of *n* specimens. From a
number of sample ranges, say 50, the average range is calculated and then multiplied by a factor (A$'_{.025}$) given in the
table, Appendix IV, to obtain the inner, and by another factor
(A$'_{.001}$) to obtain the outer, limits. For samples of 5, for instance,
these factors are ·377 and ·594 respectively. These are the
distances to be set out on both sides of the average $\overline{X}$ to give
the control limits for the averages.

Numerical example for obtaining control limits. (To be set off
from Grand Averages in the $\pm$ directions.)

Sample No.	Sample Qualities					Average of five Specimens	Ranges
(1)	5	3	2	4	6	4·0	4
(2)	6	7	5	4	5	5·4	3
(3)	3	6	3	4	5	4·2	3
(4)	8	3	7	5	4	5·4	5
(5)	6	2	6	4	5	4·6	4

Grand Average, $\overline{X}$ 4·72   Av. Range, $\overline{w}$ 3·8

* see Appendix II for the calculation of Mean and Standard Deviation

(a) Control limits obtained from *average range*, $\overline{w}_n$:

$\qquad$ 1/40 Control Limits $\quad : \overline{w}_n \times A'_{.025}$

$\qquad$ For our example $\quad : 3{\cdot}8 \times {\cdot}377 = 1{\cdot}43$

$\qquad$ 1/1000 Control Limits $\;:\; w_n \times A'_{.001}$

$\qquad$ For our example $\quad : 3{\cdot}8 \times {\cdot}594 = 2{\cdot}26$

Sample No.	Differences from respective sample means					Sums of squared deviations	Standard deviations (s) obtained as square roots of mean sums of squares
(1)	1	1	2	2	2	10·0	1·41
(2)	·6	1·6	·4	1·4	·4	5·2	1·02
(3)	1·2	1·8	1·2	·2	·8	6·8	1·16
(4)	2·6	2·4	1·1	·4	1·4	17·2	1·96
(5)	1·4	2·6	1·4	·6	·4	11·2	1·50
							$\bar{s}_5 = 6{\cdot}95 : 5 = 1{\cdot}39$

(b) Control Limits obtained from *average standard deviation* within samples.

$\qquad$ 1/40 Control Limits $\quad : \bar{s}_5 \times A_{.025}$

$\qquad$ For our example $\quad : 1{\cdot}39 \times 1{\cdot}04 = 1{\cdot}45$

$\qquad$ 1/1000 Control Limits $: \bar{s}_5 \times A_{.001}$

$\qquad$ For our example $\quad : 1{\cdot}39 \times 1{\cdot}64 = 2{\cdot}28$

(The differences in the second decimal place are due to the small number of observations and to the range function applying strictly only to normal universes.)

The factors by which to multiply the range are calculated by utilizing the above-mentioned relation between the distribution of individuals and that of averages.

The way in which they are obtained can be explained briefly as follows.

We know how to arrive at the standard deviation of the bulk from the sample range, because the function which connects these quantities is known. We merely divide the average sample range $\overline{w}$ by a certain factor, d_n, which is listed in the table,

Appendix III, and which for samples of 5 is 2·326. We further know that 3·09 times the standard deviation will give half the range of the individuals in the bulk, and therefore $\dfrac{3·09\bar{w}_n}{d_n\sqrt{n}}$,

or for samples of 5, $\dfrac{3·09\bar{w}_5}{2·326\sqrt{5}}$ will give half the range of the averages. Now it is just these values of 3·09 divided by the $d_n \times \sqrt{n}$, which are listed in Appendix IV for the 1 in 1000 limits, and a similar deduction applies to the 1 in 40 limits. These are the " factors " by which to multiply the average range $\bar{w}_n$. If instead of the range the standard deviation is calculated for each sample of n, the A-factors of Appendix IV should be used for transforming the average standard deviation in samples of $n(\bar{s}_n)$ into the distances of the control lines.

It is emphasized that the limits should be recalculated from time to time, say every 50 samples.

2.9 The Relation Between the Variation in the Bulk of Articles Produced and the Control Limits Obtained from Samples—The Rail Lines of Chance

We now understand how the actual control limits for averages are arrived at, and have now to decide whether these control limits comply with the specifications. They will do so if they are in such a position that if all averages fall within these limits, the total of the bulk will be within the specifications.

This will be the case if they more or less coincide with the 1/40 and 1/1000 limits respectively for sample averages from a 100 per cent. perfect bulk (see paragraph 2.7).

It is recommended that these theoretical limits, which are approximately obtained as $\pm\dfrac{t_u - t_l}{3}\dfrac{}{\sqrt{n}}$ and $\pm\dfrac{t_u - t_l}{2}\dfrac{}{\sqrt{n}}$, should be put together with the specification mean into the margin of the chart, and that they should be compared with the actual limits obtained from the samples as regards absolute distance and position.

Conversely, if we wanted to arrive at the true bulk limits from the control limits, all we have to do is to multiply the distance between the upper and lower 1 in 1000 limits by the square root of the sample size, and to compare that distance with the specification. The distance should not be greater than that provided by the specification tolerances, and the position of that distance should approximately be that required by the specification—that is, symmetrically around the specification Mean.

Furthermore, assuming a bulk of perfect product—that is, product within the specification—we know that the standard deviation in such a distribution is approximately $\frac{t_u - t_l}{6}$. We also know that, in order to arrive from the standard deviation at the average range of samples of n in such a bulk, we have to multiply it by a factor d_u given in Appendix III. Doing this, we arrive at a figure for the average sample range in such perfect product. This affords a sort of gauge value for the actual average range, which must not be greater than that gauge value if the product is to be within specifications. For samples of 4, say, we have $\overline{w}_4 = \sigma \times 2 \cdot 06$, or $\frac{t_u - t_l}{6 \cdot 18} \times 2 \cdot 06 = \cdot 33 \ (t_u - t_l)$ (6·18 is the value which corresponds exactly to the 1/1000 probability level).

As a routine test we should, as has been shown in paragraph 2.7, arrive at what may be called ideal control lines by calculating them from σ_A, the standard deviation of averages from the perfect bulk, put them as dotted lines on the chart or in the margin, and compare their position with the control lines actually obtained. If the product is to be satisfactory, then the actual control lines should be within the band indicated by the dotted lines, and the proportion of points inside and outside the 1/40 and 1/1000 limits in conformity with the denomination of these lines.

All these ways of satisfying ourselves as to the quality of the product are only different expressions of one and the same relationship, viz. the relationship between the standard deviation in the frequency distribution of individuals and in that of averages.

Only if the actual control limits comply with these requirements, with no more than approximately 1 in 40 and 1 in 1000 averages falling outside the corresponding limits, are we justified in saying that the process is not only stable, but the product also within specification, and only then will the control lines serve as safe " Rails of Chance."

They may be looked upon as " Rails of Chance," because, separating for a given process the area of averages which is compatible with the specifications from the "forbidden" area for such averages, they define hereby the "railway" for the process to move in. They tend to make the control inspection independent of the chance fluctuations of individual measurements by eliminating the effect upon the judgment of the examiner, of the pebbles, cobble-stones, and even stumbling blocks of freak deviations, and thus enable the process to run smoothly and uniformly as if " on rails." They are guiding lines for inspection and, thereby, for the process itself, points falling outside the control limits indicating the need for action.

2.10 Assignable Causes Versus Chance Causes—Examples of Charts

We are now in a position to distinguish between two kinds of assignable causes—statistical and economical. These two causes are not absolutely different from one another, although they represent different concepts. A statistically assignable cause may also be an economic assignable cause, but need not, and vice versa. We can, however, think of configurations on the charts which would allow us to distinguish clearly between these two types of causes.

To fix our ideas let us think of the manufacture of cartridges. Into the outer base of the cartridge case the circular " cap " is inserted containing priming composition. The correct depth of insertion is of very great importance for the functioning of the cartridge. Let us assume that the specifications for that characteristic demand that, measured from the base of the case, the cap should not be nearer than 9 thousandths of an inch and not farther than 15 thousandths of an inch. We can express this by saying that the specifications are ·012 in $\pm$ ·003 in. From the total admissible range of ·006 in. the 1/1000 control limits for samples of 5 from the specification bulk were obtained according to paragraph 2.7 and put into the margin of the chart as guiding lines in Figs. 2.6 to 2.14. Each dot on the diagrams represents an average of 5 observed depths of intrusion, the samples of 5 being taken in intervals of one quarter of an hour.

In the following diagrams the 1/1000 limits are represented by full, the 1/40 limits by broken lines.

(*a*) *Statistical and Economic Control.*—The following chart is an example of a process under control, statistical as well as economical, because not only are there no points beyond the 1/1000 limit, but the position of these limits satisfies the gauge lines in the margin of the chart.

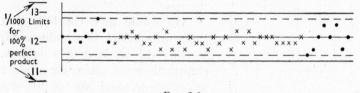

FIG. 2.6

Control Chart Picture of Process which is under Statistical
and Economic Control

(The change from dots to crosses or circles in this and the following diagrams indicates a change in shift.)

(*b*) *Lack of Statistical Control between Samples of n Items.*—The following chart shows lack of statistical control, because a considerable number of averages fall beyond the control limits. Be it observed that the variability of the product *within* samples which is epitomized by the distance between the 1/1000 limits is not far from what it should be according to the gauge limits in the margin.

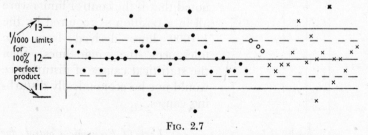

FIG. 2.7

Control Chart for Averages of Process lacking Statistical Control

(*c*) *Lack of Statistical Control between Sub-groups.*—Let us suppose that the control chart has been for some time in

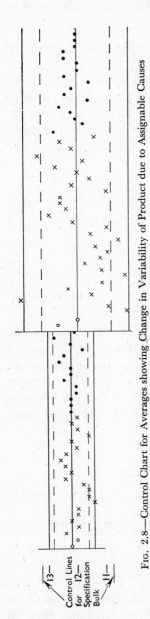

FIG. 2.8—Control Chart for Averages showing Change in Variability of Product due to Assignable Causes

operation, and that the control limits were recalculated at certain specified intervals, for instance, at the beginning of each shift or with each new batch of components put into production, and let us further suppose that the control chart represents a picture as in Fig. 2.8, with the control limits varying from one of these specified intervals to the next.

We would then conclude that there was a lack of stability, and so infer the working of assignable statistical causes, taking the product as a whole, and we could also discover the type of assignable cause. If the intervals were shift intervals we would infer that the operation differed from one team of workers to another. If, on the other hand, the intervals represented different batches of components, we would infer from a chart like that above that there was a considerable variation in the quality of components. But it should be noted that if the control limits were all in a position as required by the 1/1000 lines derived from the tolerances (the gauge lines), then the statistical causes of disturbance would not be economically disturbing causes.

(d) *Lack of Economic Control due to Faulty Setting.*—The chart, after having been for some time in operation, may have this appearance :

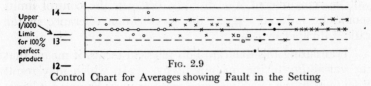

FIG. 2.9

Control Chart for Averages showing Fault in the Setting

Here we see that the control limits, although stable through-out and therefore not admitting the inference of a statistically disturbing cause, are yet not in a position which would promise an economically desirable product. Instead of being placed symmetrically around the mean (12) they are on one side (upper side) so near the specification that part of the bulk of the product must be expected to lie outside the specifications.

There is therefore an economic assignable cause present, and apparently the fault lies with the setting. The machine is set on the high side.

(e) *Lack of Economic Control due to Increased Variability.*—Another assignable economic cause of disturbance can be inferred from a diagram like this :

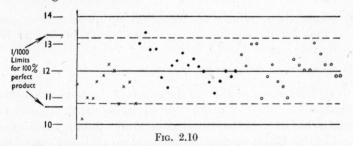

FIG. 2.10

Control Chart for Averages showing a Process which is under Statistical but not under Economic Control

Whereas in Fig. 2.9 the absolute distance between the control limits was considerably less than the specification range, indicating that it was not the variability of the machine but only the setting which was at fault, we find in this diagram that the distance between the control limits is so wide as to bring these limits right up to the specifications. From what was said above, this means that a considerable part of the bulk must be expected to lie outside the specifications, because, as will be remembered, the distance between the control limits should be reduced against the specification tolerance in the ratio 1 divided by $\sqrt{n}$.

Translating this diagram into physical terms, it means that the variability of the machine is too great, which may result from tools in the machine being worn or parts having got loose. In order to verify conclusions like those mentioned in this paragraph, which were arrived at by mere inspection of the chart, we have to apply the methods given in the preceding paragraph.

For instance, the ideal control limits derived from the tolerances which we put into the margin of the chart, together with the specification mean, enable us to check the quality of the product at a glance, not only as regards its general level but also as regards its variability. For more precise information we would apply one of the numerical methods.

2.11 Modified Technique of Control *

In this paragraph useful modifications of the Control Chart method will be outlined for the extreme cases where the variability of the product was

(1) *greater* than admissible according to specifications, and could by no engineering or other means be further reduced ; or

(2) *smaller* than required by specifications.

(1) Let us assume that all the efforts of the production man to reduce the range of manufactured product with regard to a certain characteristic have been of no avail. Simply to abandon the Control Chart method is obviously no real way out of the difficulty, because this would not by itself improve the quality of the product. What we must try in such a case is to make control feasible and useful by either changing the specifications or the method of control.

If it was essential that the characteristic should be controlled around the specification mean, *both* tolerances being of equal importance, then there is no other way of bringing actual production and specifications into line with one another

* see *First Guide of Quality Control for Engineers*, Ministry of Supply (H.M.S.O., 1946)

than the reconsideration of the latter, and a suggestion to that effect should be forwarded to the management.

If on, the other hand, it was not the mean but only *one* of the tolerances which was of vital importance in order that the product should be usable, then the following modification of the control method is recommended.

It can be used, for instance, with success in the process of cap insertion if, whether for reasons in the components or for engineering reasons, the sample range became incompatible with the specifications. Considering that insufficient depth of insertion is a rectifiable fault, whereas excessive depth is an incurable one, the upper tolerance is regarded as the " vital " one in the sense of the method now to be explained.

Let us keep in mind :

(*a*) that if practically no part of the product must fall beyond the vital tolerance, the mean of the distribution of measurements must lie—normality assumed—at a distance of 3.09σ or $3.09\dfrac{1}{d_n}\overline{w}$ from that tolerance. The value of our variable obtained in this way we regard as the mean, $\overline{X}$, around which we now try to control the characteristic.

(*b*) that if the $1/1000$ limits are obtained in the usual way, by measuring the distance $A'\overline{w}_n$ from that Mean, $\overline{X}$, they represent the allowable range of sample means if practically no individual measurements were to fall beyond the vital tolerance. These, then, are the control lines by which to work.

We can express this in a somewhat different way. If, no matter how great the average range, $\overline{w}_n$ in our samples of n was, we wanted to exclude the possibility of individuals falling outside the vital tolerance, be it the upper or the lower, then the $1/1000$ limit must not come nearer to our tolerance than the distance $\dfrac{\text{Bulk Range} - \text{Range of Means}}{2}$ in symbols, $3.09\dfrac{1}{d_n}\overline{w}$

$- A'_{.001}\overline{w}_n$, or $\overline{w}_n(3.09\dfrac{1}{d_n} - A'_{.001})$ because even the extreme outliers of the distribution of sample means, lying close to the $1/1000$ limit, do not contain individuals more than 3.09σ or

$3 \cdot 09 \dfrac{1}{d_n} \, \overline{w}_n$ distant from the mean of the parent distribution (normality of the distribution assumed), which deviation would exceed the vital tolerance.

The factors $(3 \cdot 09 \dfrac{1}{d_n} - A'_{.001})$ denoted by the letter M, by which we multiply the average range, $\overline{w}$, in order to obtain the required distance from the vital tolerance, are listed in a little table at the end of this paragraph for samples from 2 to 10.

Adopting this version of the control method, we measure the quantities so obtained as distances from the important tolerance (the upper, in our case), inwards, which gives our theoretical 1/1000 control line. As that limit is always $A'_{.001}\overline{w}_n$ distant from the distribution mean, $\overline{X}$, we obtain the latter by measuring $A'_{.001}\overline{w}_n$ from the control limit inwards, that is, towards the other tolerance.

This modification will be found extremely useful under the circumstances described above, provided any change in the variability of the product is immediately taken account of by recalculation of the 1/1000 limits and the working mean.

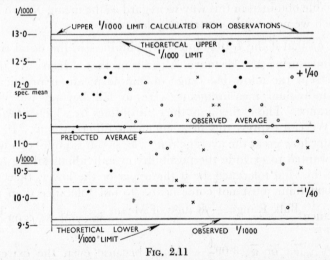

FIG. 2.11

Control Chart of Process which has to be controlled with regard to the Upper Tolerance and around a Working Mean (as different from the Specification Mean). Observe how closely the average and 1/1000 limits calculated from the observations approach the theoretical average and control lines

(2) Where the variability of the product is considerably smaller than required by specification tolerances, the control chart will often show a fluctuating mean. This, however, should not be taken as a peculiarity of the distribution, which is better than it need be. But it is only in a case like this that we are in a position to make allowance for a fluctuating mean without employing too elaborate methods. A case like this arises in the process we have chosen as an illustration, if both the quality of the components and the precision of the machine are above average.

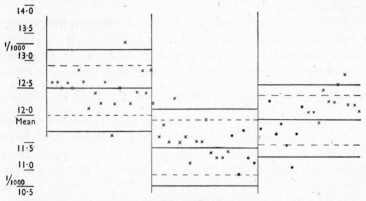

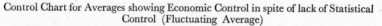

Fig. 2.12

Control Chart for Averages showing Economic Control in spite of lack of Statistical Control (Fluctuating Average)

According to the strict letter of instruction, the quality controller would have to advise adjustment of the machine or alteration of the operation whenever a point falls outside the 1/1000 limits, which happens fairly often in such a case if the limits are obtained from a great number of samples. He would then probably meet with the objection on the part of production or those servicing the machine that there was no need for correction as the product was within specifications. Looking at the control lines in the margin of the chart, we could not help admitting that the distribution of plotted points did not exceed these limits for 100 per cent. perfect product in spite of the instability of the process.

It is thus obvious that the 1/1000 control limits obtained

from an average range, $\overline{w}$, which was better than the specifications require it to be, would tend to make the control of the characteristic stricter than it need be, because it does not tolerate instability even though it was not harmful to the quality of the product.

In order to avoid such unnecessary hardship, we use a somewhat similar device as in case (1). There we removed the 1/1000 limit a suitable distance from the tolerance, and here we shall make it approach the tolerances as much as is compatible with bringing practically none of the product outside specifications.

We can allow for a shifting mean by working to the extreme 1/1000 limits that could result from the observed variability of the product. Such limits are obtained by measuring from each of the tolerances inwards (towards the centre of the distribution) the distance $\overline{w}_n$ $(3\cdot09\,\dfrac{1}{d_n} - A'_{.001})$ or $\overline{w}_nM$, because, assuming a constant variability smaller than required by specifications, *no* sample of n whose average falls within these limits will contain individual measurements outside specifications. These limits are simply the 1/1000 limits of the partial distributions around the extreme mean values which can be tolerated if practically nothing is to lie outside specifications.

Here, too, the warning must be added that the method will

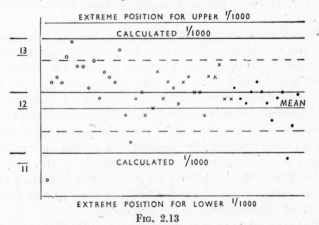

Fig. 2.13

Control Chart for Averages with 1/1000 Limits set in from Specification Tolerances

be found useful only if the variability of the product is checked at suitable intervals, and the position of the limits recalculated should changes in that variability occur.

TABLE 2.1

Factors M by which to multiply the average range, $\bar{w}_n$, in order to obtain the distance nearer than which the 1/1000 limit is not to approach a tolerance if the product is still to be within specifications (to be applied only if the precision of the process is higher than required or implied by the specifications, and (para. 2.11 (1)) where the process is controlled around an artificial or working mean shifted so as to suit the excessive variability of the process).

No. in Sample (n)	2	3	4	5	6	7	8	9	10
Factor (M_n)	·80	·77	·75	·73	·72	·71	·70	·69	·69

(Factors are calculated according to the formula :

$$\frac{\frac{1}{2}\,\text{Bulk Range} - \frac{1}{2}\,\text{Range of Sample Means}}{\bar{w}_n}$$

$$= \left(\frac{3\cdot09\,\bar{w}_n}{d_n} - \frac{3\cdot09\,\bar{w}_n}{d_n\sqrt{n}}\right)\Big/\bar{w}_n$$

$$= \frac{3\cdot09}{d_n} - A'_{0\cdot001})$$

2.12 Trends

Before we leave the subject of charts of averages, there is one more point to be discussed, and that is trends of plotted points on the chart indicative of certain undesirable conditions of the process.

The basic rule for quality control, that the plotted points should be within the control limits, and that the control limits should be in a position satisfying the specifications, needs to be completed by certain minor rules which will prove helpful for spotting trouble in time.

A chart may present a picture like this :

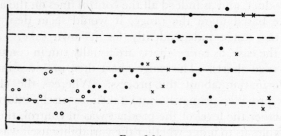

FIG. 2.14
Control Chart showing Trend

In this chart none of the points plotted falls outside the control limits which, let us suppose, are in a satisfactory position with regard to specifications, but in the left half we notice a definite trend of the points towards the upper limit. A picture like this indicates that the processs has lost stability, and that the product will be unsatisfactory if this trend is allowed to go on. If such a trend is observed, the machine must be stopped and the cause of the trouble investigated. As a rule it will be a variable cause which is correlated with the characteristic measured. Such a correlation disturbs the normal variability of the product and should not be tolerated.

In the right half we see that the product, although within the control limits, has all piled up towards the upper limit. As the upper limit is, according to our assumption, in a satisfactory position, this does not mean that part of the product will be out of specifications, but it does indicate that it will be all on the high side of specifications, and such components have been found unsatisfactory in a subsequent assembling process. One should aim at a symmetrical distribution of the points around the mean, thinning out towards the control lines. The discovery of trends is made easier by working with averages instead of with individual measurements. Fluctuations *within* samples are averaged out in this way, and the real differences *between* samples brought out more clearly. The subject of " Trends " will be fully dealt with in Chapter V.

2.13 Range Charts

From what has been said hitherto, the importance of the range has doubtless emerged. As so much depends on the range of the product, and as indeed all the control lines on the average chart are based upon the range, it would seem desirable to control the range independently for its own sake. This is actually the case, as range charts are usually run in conjunction with average charts. The range chart then provides independent information about the process. Whereas the chart of averages provides primarily, and taken by itself, information as to whether the level of the product was in control, the range chart enables us to judge whether the variability itself was under control. It should be remembered, however, that the range enters into the construction of the control lines for averages. These, as we have seen, are obtained from the average range of samples of n, and their distance and position give valuable information about the spread of measurements.

Control limits 1 in 40 and 1 in 1000 are calculated for the range charts according to a method analagous to that described for the chart of averages. They are obtained, like the control limits for the average chart, from the average range by multiplying that quantity by certain factors given in the table, Appendix IV.* The statistical meaning of these limits is the same as that of the control limits on the average chart, that is, they represent the 1/40 and 1/1000 limits for sample ranges of n specimens.

As the control limits for the range vary with the sample quality, viz. are pushed up by bad and lowered by good quality, it is essential to consider not only the question of statistical control of ranges, but also of economic control. A product which keeps well within the 1/1000 limit for ranges may be economically undesirable and disqualified as " highly defective " if those limits have been obtained from highly defective samples.

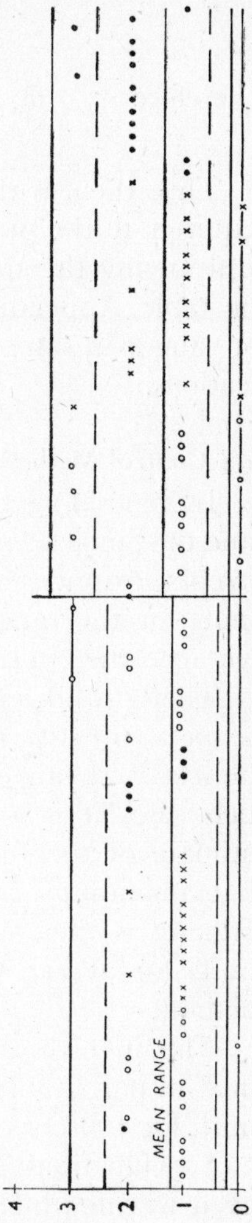

To have guidance limits in the margin of the chart whose position can be compared with that of the limits resulting from the observations is therefore just as advisable as it was for the chart of averages, if not more so. Such limits are obtained in quite a simple way. We know that the distance from the mean of the

FIG. 2.15   Control Chart for Ranges

* Factors for obtaining such limits from the Average Standard Deviation in Samples of n ($\bar{s}_n$) are given in the left half of the table

(612)

4

1/1000 limits for averages from the specification bulk (let us call it D) is given by

$$D_n = \frac{t_u - t_e}{2\sqrt{n}} = \bar{v}_n \times A'_{.001}$$

Therefore $\qquad \bar{w}_n = \frac{D_n}{A'_{.001}}$, where $D_n = \frac{t_u - t_l}{2\sqrt{n}}$

This, then, is the average range in samples of n which is required if the product is to comply with the specified level. Multiplying this quantity, $\bar{w}_n$, by the proper factors listed in the table, Appendix IV (*b*), $D'_{.999}$, we obtain the 1/1000 limit for ranges in samples of n which is compatible with the specifications.

2.14 Control Method if the Range is Specified Independently

In general we thus derive our estimate of the correct range, (and the limits for range) from the specification tolerances for the *level* of the dimension in question. That is to say, our theoretical limits for the range are obtained from a statistically derived average range in samples of n.

There is, however, a type of specification which in addition to specifying the required level of a dimension also specifies the *maximum* range in a given number of determinations. In such cases it is not only possible but necessary to base our estimate of the required average range in small samples on that maximum range allowed by the specifications. This estimate is then used for arriving at the theoretical 1/1000 limits for averages. We have thus the reverse of the usual method.

This involves using a system of control similar to that outlined in paragraph 2.11, point 2, for arriving at the theoretical limits for 100 per cent. perfect product.

Specifications may be of the following type : a range is given within which a number of determinations made on one and the same individual article for a given characteristic are allowed to vary. At the same time it is stated that the highest and lowest determination are not to differ by more than a specified amount.

As an illustration, let us assume that a paralleling lathe operation is carried out on brass discs or rings (cylinders of short height), and the specifications are that the thickness of the disc or ring, measured at any point along the periphery— that is, the distance between the upper and the lower surface— can be anything from ·405 in. to ·415 in., but with the proviso that the maximum and minimum determination on one individual article is not to differ by more than ·004 in. Let us further assume that the number of determinations to be taken on each article is fixed at eight—that is, the thickness of the cylindrical object is measured at eight equidistant points along the periphery.

In order to arrive at the control chart of averages and ranges, we consider the eight determinations taken on one article as being so many samples, and say consequently that we are working with samples of 8, whose averages we plot on the chart for averages and whose ranges we plot on the chart for ranges.

The difficulty now is this : the specification range for single measurements, ·405 in. to ·415 in. = ·010 in., is in this case evidently independent of the specified required range be-tween any co-ordinated 8 determinations, that is between the measurements taken on one and the same article, which is ·004 in.

The 1/1000 limits, calculated from the former for samples of 8, and resulting in $\pm \dfrac{t_u - t_l}{2\sqrt{n}} = \dfrac{\cdot 010 \text{ in.}}{2\sqrt{8}} = \pm \cdot 0018$ in., bear no direct relation to the allowed amount of non-parallelism of ·004 in. per article.

This is shown by the following simple consideration. The *average* range $\bar{w}$ in samples of 8 which would correspond to the distance of the 1/1000 limits from the specification mean, viz., $\pm 1\cdot 8$ thousandths inch, is evidently $1\cdot 8 \div A'_{\cdot 001}$ or $1\cdot 8 \div \cdot 384 = 4\cdot 7$ thousandths inch. But we are supposed to work to a 4·0 thousandths inch *maximum* range within samples of 8, and if the specifications are correct—that is, in conformity with what can be attained in actual work—we should be able to do so. The maximum range clearly has the function of the upper 1/1000 limit on the chart for ranges (see paragraph

2.13), and for samples of 8 we can easily obtain the average range in such samples by dividing the value of the limit, 0·004 in., by the factor $D'_{.999}$ for samples of 8 (see table, Appendix IV (*b*)), viz. 2·04, which gives ·002 in., sensibly. This is considerably less than the value for the average range resulting from the first part of the specifications, viz. ·0047 in. The implication is that the specifications make due allowance for the mean to vary to a somewhat greater extent than can be accounted for by fluctuations of sampling only. It follows in the light of what has been said in the preceding paragraph 2.11 that we should allow the averages, and thus the 1/1000 limits, to approach nearer to the specifications than would correspond to a 4·7 thousandths in. range in samples of 8, namely, as near as corresponds to a 2 thousandths in. average range in such samples.

All we have to do is to determine the distance from each tolerance at which the 1/1000 limit (and, therefore, the plotted averages) could still lie if the product was to be within specifications. The extreme averages, if they are still to comply with the specifications, should be distant from the tolerance by not less than $\frac{1}{2}$ bulk range $-\frac{1}{2}$ sample average range, or

$$3\cdot09\sigma - 3\cdot09\ \frac{\sigma}{\sqrt{n}} = \frac{3\cdot09\ \bar{w}_8}{d_8} - \frac{3\cdot09\ \bar{w}_8}{d_8\sqrt{8}} = \frac{3\cdot09\times\cdot002}{2\cdot85} - \frac{3\cdot09\times\cdot002}{2\cdot8\times2\cdot85}$$

$= \cdot00271$ in. $- \cdot00077$ in. $= \cdot0014$ in. 1·4 thousandths in.,

then, is the distance farther than which a 1/1000 limit, obtained from actual work, and set in from tolerances is not to be distant from either tolerance if the product is to comply with both parts of the specifications. This, as will be seen from the following diagram (Fig. 2.16), increases the allowable range for sample averages by more than 3 thousandths in., and prevents our having to ask for machine adjustment without the product falling outside specifications.

But these " 1/1000 limits " have here a somewhat different meaning from those encountered in paragraph 2.11.

There they were calculated from the *observed* average range in samples of *n*, which happened to be smaller than the average range for such samples when obtained theoretically from the specifications. They represented the " top limits " in either

direction from the mean for either averages or 1/1000 limits
obtained from the averages ; anything *within* was acceptable.
They may be said to have the function of being the " limits
of limits," and remain what they are as long as the average
range is the same.

Here, however, they are obtained from a range which
explicitly is part of the specifications and as such is constant.
In our case, it was the average range between any eight
measurements taken on one and the same article, viz. ·002 in.
The actual average range in such samples of eight determinations may be better or worse. If better, the limits will be
nearer to the specification tolerances, if worse, they will be
farther away. The " 1/1000 limits " which we obtain from
both parts of the specifications and, as usual, put into the
margin of the chart as guiding lines, have thus here the function
of a " bottom limit " in either direction from the mean as far
as observed 1/1000 limits are concerned (not as far as single
averages are concerned).

A 1/1000 limit obtained from the actual observations
according to paragraph 2.11, and set in from the specification

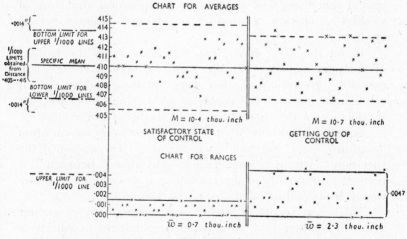

FIG. 2.16

Control Chart for Process with Specified Level and Specified Range
Specifications : *single* measurements between ·405″ and ·415″; *difference* between
determinations made on one and the same article must not exceed ·004″

tolerances must not approach the specification mean nearer than those limits. If it does it is not acceptable, because it implies a greater range than that specified.

The theoretical limits which we obtained here may be said to have the function of being " limits to modified limits " or bottom limits to the top limits of 1/1000 limits.

The following control charts for average and range of samples of 8 thickness determinations per ring, the sampling incidence being one ring every half-hour, will help to make this somewhat involved relationship clearer (Fig. 2.16).

2.15 Variation "Within" and "Between" Samples (or Sub-groups)

In drawing conclusions from the range chart we must always be careful as to whether the variations in range occur within or between the sub-groups or the samples of n specimens.

Sub-groups of samples may be made, for instance, according to batches of components or according to shifts. If we find the average range varying significantly from one of these sub-groups to the next, we would conclude in the first case that there was a difference in the quality of components so far as it affects the characteristic for which we measure, and in the second that there was a difference in operation, one team of workers producing a product of greater uniformity than another.

If, on the other hand, the variations *within* the batches of components, or *within* the teams of operatives, was appreciably greater than that between these sub-groups, it would indicate that the condition of machine tools was not satisfactory, or that parts of the machine had become loose.

Equally important is the distinction between variation " within " and " between " samples of n. In general, if the variation " within " was greater than that " between " it pointed to instability of the machine ; if it was the other way round, it pointed to instability of the operation.

This very important matter will be discussed in greater detail in Chapter IV. Be it noted here that the possibility of distinguishing between those two kinds of variation as afforded by the control chart method is due to the working with sample averages instead of with individuals.

2.16 The Meaning of Working with Averages in Industrial Control Inspection

It is very important for the understanding of the quality control chart to realize how closely is the working with averages, instead of with individual observations, bound up with the problem of distinguishing between chance and assignable causes.

We have referred to the taking of samples of a certain size at specified intervals, temporal or numerical, as the sub-grouping of observations. Let us be clear about the meaning of the term " sub-group."

Arranging individual articles into one frequency distribution by recording the number of measurements falling into successive class intervals of our scale is called " grouping the observations."

We may, however, prefer to take a number of observations, say n, or, in other words, a sample of n units, and group these samples according to some quantitative characteristic. This means that we sub-divide the total into as many secondary groups as there are samples of n units.

The term " sub-group " is also used for batches of product proceeding from different sources such as different shifts, different machines, different lots of components, etc., and helps to differentiate between such collections of samples as are intermediate between the total and the proper samples of n units.

The question now arises : How do we know what sub-group to use ? What shall be the sample size and what the interval—also called the sampling incidence—and why make sub-groups at all ?

Now, the second type of sub-group referred to above gives us a hint for answering these questions.

Within a shift or within the product coming from one machine only, or within one lot of components, there should be no variations apart from those due to chance causes which, in a certain sense, are unavoidable variations. But it is quite conceivable that the operation may differ from shift to shift because one team of operatives may work better than another ; that a machine might have worn tools and work less reliably than others ; and that lots of components may differ in quality. The sub-division into batches of samples coming from conceivably different sources, and the comparison of the average quality of these batches, will now make it possible to differentiate between them with regard to the quality of the product, and to locate trouble at the source as a preliminary to improvement.

This is also the principle of the further finer sub-grouping by taking samples of n and working with their averages.

These sub-groups (in samples of n units) should be chosen so as to break up the total into groups of such size and intervals that *within* them variations may, for engineering reasons, be considered to be due to chance causes only, but *between* which there may be differences due to assignable causes whose presence is considered possible. Working with sub-groups and samples of n instead of with the total and the individual observations, then, enables us to distinguish between chance and assignable causes.

The full power of the method of working with averages instead of with individuals will become apparent in Chapter IV.

The fundamental principle of the control chart technique is thus that we take small samples, from 4 to 10, in specified regular intervals, and ascertain whether, in spite of the nonrandomness of sampling, the total of samples complies with the requirements of randomness (judging by the behaviour of sample averages and measures of spread). If so, we are satisfied that we are dealing with a chance cause system, or, as we say, that the process is under control.

With this purpose in view, we make the sampling incidence (intervals between samples) such as would most likely show up any cause of disturbance or non-randomness. These intervals we specify according to what is known about the variability of the process, that is, according to the time, or number of manufactured articles, it would take the suspected disturbing cause to make itself felt upon the characteristic in question.

When working to specifications we compare the position and distance of the observed control lines with those for the 100 per cent. perfect distribution. That is, we compare the two *means* and the two *standard deviations*. But only under one condition are we justified in drawing the conclusion that if mean and standard deviation are sensibly the same, the product will comply with the specification.

This condition is that the same *statistical law* governs both the theoretical and the observed distribution. It is fulfilled for our case if the process is under control, because this implies that it is subject to the Normal Law, and thus follows the same type of distribution which we assume to prevail in the specification bulk. Lack of control is indicated by points falling outside the control limits (in greater than the assigned proportion) and this is taken as a signal for corrective action.

CHAPTER III

THE ROD OF MOSES—PROBABILITY GRAPHS

3.1 Mathematical Tools Simplify the Application of Statistical Methods to Industrial Problems

THE method explained up to now follows the process closely. It can be described as being an almost synchronized method for recording the quality of the product.

It is, however, sometimes desirable and sufficient to have an historical picture of the quality, that is, a sort of summary of the recordings made over a certain period of time. Such a method is, for instance, suitable for sampling inspection of components delivered to the factory for the purpose of assembly, and for the examination of the finished product (especially if the characteristic for which we sample is measurable or weighable).

The principle underlying both Quality Control in the strict sense of the term and the method to be explained now, is the same. We want to obtain a reliable estimate of the bulk quality from samples taken from the bulk, and thus be able to compare the quality actually produced with the specifications.

In quality control we achieve this aim by deriving from the actual samples control limits which enable us to estimate the bulk quality, and to compare it with the specifications.

The method about to be explained goes still further as regards compactness of information. The whole information about bulk quality in relation to the specifications is now contained in a single line, whose position and direction allow us to draw certain inferences. It thus differs from the former method essentially in the degree of compactness of information, or of simplification.

It is interesting to note that, in applying these methods of control, the examiner or inspector is handling rather involved problems of probability. To do this without adequate knowledge of the theory of probability and statistical theory would be impossible had not mathematical tools been provided for handling the matter in a quick and efficient manner. These mathematical tools are so simple that the matter has become accessible to practical people engaged in the manufacturing process, and can be handled without much previous knowledge of the theory of probability.

We have already encountered one of those tools, which consists in differentiating between a pure chance distribution and a distribution disturbed by assignable causes, simply by counting the number of observations inside and outside the control lines. If the proportions of these classes of observations were those demanded by the theory of the normal curve, then we concluded that we were dealing with a chance distribution. Otherwise, we concluded that there were assignable causes interfering with the system of chance causes.

Now we are coming to a mathematical tool which simplifies the matter still more, but which has the same theoretical basis —that is, the properties of the normal curve.

3.2 The Principle of the Probability Graph *

Let us assume that a quality control chart has been in operation for some time and that individual observations only have been plotted. Looking at the following diagram we see at once that the number of points belonging to certain intervals of the vertical scale, which represents our variable character-istic, differs from one interval to the other, although sym-metrically placed intervals show approximately the same density of points.

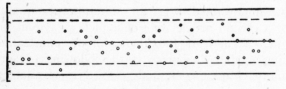

Fig. 3.1

A typical Control Chart for Individuals if the Process is under Control

We could now group the points in such a way as to obtain a frequency curve. All we have to do is to push the points

* The use of a specially constructed probability grid is due to A. Hazen (*Transactions A.S.C.E.*, 77, 1539–1640 (1914)). As a method of industrial control it was developed in the Ministry of Supply during World War II.

towards the left-hand scale while preserving the vertical distance of a point from the origin of that scale, rotate the chart back from where we started—paragraph 2.3—that is, through an angle of 90°, and erect over the intervals rectangles whose area is proportional to the number of points belonging to that interval. We can now what is called " sum " the area of the curve from one end to the other simply by putting one rectangle on top of the other, adding thus the frequency of all the intervals successively. Joining the tops of the rectangles thus obtained, we arrive at an S-shaped curve called the ogive or cumulative curve.

What follows now is reminiscent of the Biblical story according to which the snake writhing on the ground was transformed into a straight rod when the fearless hand of Moses lifted it off the ground. It is possible to transform the wriggly shape of our curve into a straight line by choosing suitable intervals on the vertical scale, such as will stretch that curve into a straight line. All one need do for that purpose is to space the intervals, not equally as in Fig. 3.1, but according to the probability integral or the Error Function. Tables for that function are available which tell us the percentage of observations which is expected to lie up to a certain distance either on both sides of the mean or from the left-hand start of the curve. Graph paper constructed on these lines is commercially obtainable, from which we can read what percentage of observations is expected to lie within a given distance from the left-hand origin of the cumulative curve.

If we now wanted to get an estimate of the quality of the bulk of a certain article we would pick a random sample of sufficient size, at least 100, then plot the cumulative curve, according to the rules given in the following paragraph, on Probability Graph paper, and proceed to translate the geometrical picture so obtained into physical terms.

As seen from the following diagram, there is a point marked 50 on the right-hand scale, meaning 50 per cent. of the distribution. Projecting that point on to the line representing our sample, and then projecting the crossing-point on to the horizontal scale, we read on that scale the mean of the distribution. Furthermore, projecting the point marked 16 or

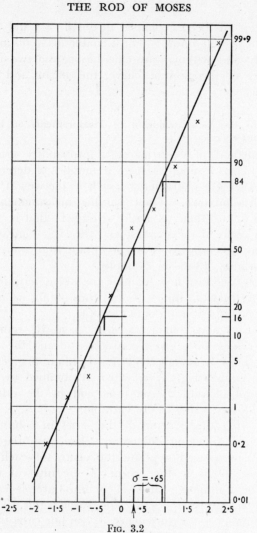

FIG. 3.2

The Probability Graph

84 on the right-hand scale on to our line, and again projecting the crossing-point vertically downwards, we read on our scale the Standard Deviation, as the distance of that point from the mean.

Why this is so will become clear when the construction of

the diagram has been explained in detail (3.3 and 3.7). All
that should be noted now is that it enables us to obtain, merely
graphically and without any calculation, the two important
parameters of the normal curve, the mean and standard
deviation.

3.3 How to Plot a Distribution of Measurements on Probability Graph Paper

The method of constructing a probability graph is as
follows. Let us assume we have a number of determinations
taken on a certain characteristic such as the weight of a component of a mixture. These varying measurements of our
characteristic are then, as a rule, grouped—that is, we divide
the range between the smallest and the largest measurements
into at least 10 equal parts and so obtain 10 or more intervals
for our variable (13 in our example).

We now ascertain how many of the 327 determinations fall
into each of these 13 intervals, and thus obtain what is called
the frequency distribution of our sample.

Columns 1 and 2 in Table 3.1a (page 51) represent the
range of values for a given characteristic and the frequency
distribution for a sample of 327. Column 3 gives what is
called the cumulative curve, which is obtained by summing
the series of column 2 from one end to the other, starting at the lowest value of the variable.

Comparing the position of the series in columns 2 and
3 we see the following difference. The class frequencies of
column 2 are placed opposite the centre of each interval,
for instance 69 being the centre of the interval 68 to 70,
whereas the cumulative values of column 3 are placed opposite
the end of each class interval. The reason is this. The grouping of a number of measurements, 327 in our case, into a considerably smaller number of intervals, introduces an element of
uncertainty. As we are only interested in whether a weighing
falls into one group or another, the weighing in one interval
can range from the lower limit to the upper limit of that interval.

In order to be able to treat these observations as having a
definite value, which is essential for calculating the parameters
of the distribution, they are by convention placed against the

TABLE 3.1a — Observed distribution

Weight (in grains)	No. of samples corresponding	Cumulative series	Cumulative %	Frequency %
69	4			1·2
		4	1·2	
71	17			5·2
		21	6·4	
73	39			11·9
		60	18·3	
75	62			19·0
		122	37·3	
77	58			17·7
		180	55·0	
79	52			16·0
		232	71·0	
81	35			11·0
		267	82·0	
83	22			6·7
		289	88·7	
85	18			5·3
		309	94·0	
87	13			4·0
		320	98·0	
89	4			1·1
		324	99·1	
91	2			0·6
		326	99·7	
93	1			0·3
	327	327	100·0	

TABLE 3.1b — Theoretical distribution

Weight (in grains)	Deviation from M	Deviation standardized	Cumulative %	Frequency %
				4·0
70	−8	1·77	4	
				5·0
72	−6	1·33	9	
				10·0
74	−4	·88	19	
				14·0
76	−2	·44	33	
				17·0
78	0	0	50	
				17·0
80	2	·44	67	
				14·0
82	4	·88	81	
				10·0
84	6	1·33	91	
				5·0
86	8	1·77	96	
				2·8
88	10	2·22	98·8	
				0·8
90	12	2·66	99·6	
				0·3
92	14	3·11	99·91	
				0·1
94	16	3·55	99·98	

$$M = 78 \cdot 00 \qquad \sigma = 4 \cdot 51$$

centre of the interval, and this is the value which is given to them.

If it now comes to summing up the area under the curve represented in column 2 from one end to the other, we must, in order to arrive finally at the end of the last interval, proceed in steps of whole intervals, starting at the end of the first interval and then going on to the end of the second, end of third, and so on. Our cumulative values are therefore to be placed not against the central value of the interval, but against the end of each interval. This has the effect of shifting series column **3** upwards by half an interval.

Column **4** gives the reduction of the series in column **3** to 100 in our case, by dividing each value by $3 \cdot 27$. The figures in column **4** then represent percentages, and it is these percentages which are plotted on the probability graph.

3.4 The Effect of Grouping

Let us dwell a little while on the effect of " grouping." It is evident that the size of the interval will have an effect upon the shape of the distribution and thereby upon its parameters. The question now arises : What governs the size of the interval; and secondly, how does grouping as such affect the distribution ?

1. Whenever we are taking measurements of a certain dimension, the intervals of the scale according to which we want to group the measurements are dependent on the precision of the measuring instrument. If, say, the instrument measures to a precision of $\pm \cdot 5$ thousandths of an inch, then there would be no use in having a scale with class intervals of less than $\cdot 5$ thousandths, although the actual precise dimensions do not jump by $\cdot 5$ thousandths in. but vary continuously.

All one can do in such a case is to take the attainable precision of the instrument as representing the minimum value of the class interval of the scale. What this amounts to is that we take the centre of a class interval of the attainable precision to represent the value of the variable.

What is necessity in this case becomes a convention when we are dealing with variables which we find it advisable to group into much larger intervals than would correspond to the precision of the measuring instrument, because what matters economically in such cases is only a certain interval of the variable. We then treat these intervals as if they were the intervals attainable by the precision of measuring and regard the centre of the interval as representing the value of the observations falling into that interval.

2. Within each interval there will be a miniature frequency distribution, with a mean value somewhere near the centre of the interval and a total range equal to the interval itself.

Assuming each such distribution to be normal, we could take the centre of the interval as representing the mean. This is the theoretical basis for regarding the interval centre as representing the value of all observations falling into that interval.

But it is clear from the shape of the total normal distribution that the distribution within the intervals will differ from normal ; the values near the inner end of the interval will always be more frequent than those near the outer end. The actual mean of each interval will therefore be displaced towards the inner end of the intervals. This necessitates a correction of the standard deviation obtained under the assumption of normality of the interval distributions, by subtracting from the squared standard deviation $\dfrac{c^2}{12}$ where c is the number of units per interval. This correction is called, after its originator, Sheppard's correction.

3.5 The Distinction Between Bulk (Population) and Sample Quality (I) —The Chi-Square Test

We have now to consider whether the straight line probability graph can be taken to represent adequately the bulk from which the sample came. The problem has two stages :

1. Taking the mean and standard deviation of our sample to be those of the bulk, can the line be regarded as a reasonably good representation of that bulk distribution ? ; and

2. To what extent are we justified in identifying the mean and standard deviation of our sample with those of the bulk of the product in which we are ultimately interested ?

These questions will be dealt with in this and the following paragraphs.

The implication of the Straight Line Probability Graph is that the line represents a bulk with the same mean and standard deviation as we have found to characterize our sample. There will be, as a rule, deviations between the class frequencies of our sample and those of the theoretical bulk distribution, and the question is now whether the deviations resulting in a particular case can be regarded as being due to fluctuations of chance only, or whether they are too great to comply with our assumption that the straight line graph really respresents the bulk from which our sample came.

Considering that a normal distribution is entirely determined by the two parameters, mean (M) and standard deviation (σ), we construct (instead of drawing it free-hand) the straight-line probability graph representing a normal distribution with the same M and σ as our sample, as a preliminary to carrying out the test.

All we have to do for that purpose is to standardize the class intervals measured from the distribution mean, that is, to divide the deviations of our variable from that mean by σ, read from the table or graph for the cumulative normal curve (see Appendix I) the percentages corresponding to the values $\frac{x_i}{\sigma}$ and plot these percentages on probability paper as the ordinates of the corresponding values of x_i (see also paragraph 3.7).

As an illustration let us use the data of Table 3.1, whose second half (3.1b) shows the theoretical distribution. Its cumulative percentage frequencies are nothing else but the percentages which we have read off the Probability Integral Table or Graph. They are given in column 4, whereas column 1 contains the interval ends instead of the interval centres of our original distribution (Table 3.1a), column 2 the deviations of these upper interval limits from the mean, and column 3 the standardized deviations. The frequencies of column 4 are now plotted on probability graph paper in exactly the same way as the cumulative percentage frequencies of the actual sample but without shifting the series by half an interval, as they represent already the cumulative frequencies right up to the respective interval ends.

From the *cumulative* percentage series we obtain the theoretical *frequency* distribution (column 5) by forming the differences of successive terms in the former. This series is now compared with the observed distribution reduced to a sample size of 100 (column 5, Table 3.1a).

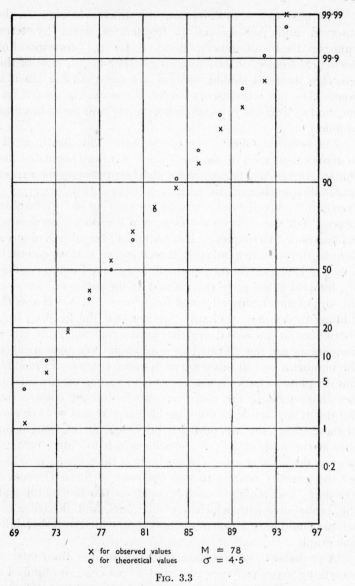

X for observed values   M = 78
o for theoretical values   σ = 4·5

FIG. 3.3

Probability Graphs of Observed and Theoretical Distributions

The next step is to determine the differences between the observed and the theoretical frequencies, term by term, squaring these differences, dividing by the corresponding theoretical frequency, and summing. (For the purpose of this test, class intervals should contain not less than five observations. The last four intervals were, therefore, contracted into one, and so were the first two, reducing the number of intervals to nine.)

The result is called χ^2 or Chi square. This function, like so many others used in statistical work, has been tabulated and charted, the horizontal axis of the chart representing the various probability levels and the vertical what is called " Degrees of Freedom." We are familiar with the concept of " Probability Levels," but the expression " Degree of Freedom " needs some explanation. If a frequency distribution of altogether N observations is grouped into n intervals, then it is clear that we can fill in only $n - 1$ interval frequencies arbitrarily ; the frequency of the nth interval is uniquely determined as the difference between the sum of the already allocated frequencies and N. If now the " filling in " is left to chance, we say that the freedom from restrictions is measured by the number of intervals whose frequencies are not dictated by anything. We thus speak of the number $n - 1$ in this sense as so many Degrees of Freedom. But the play of chance is also restricted by using certain quantities characterizing the observed distribution for constructing the theoretical series, in our case by using M and σ. For each of these constraints we subtract unity, and arrive thus in our case at the number $9 - 3 = 6$ with which to enter the table of χ^2 on the vertical scale. In the body of the table we now look for the number nearest to our observed χ^2 for 6 Degrees of Freedom, and having found it, read on the horizontal scale the probability with which a χ^2 like ours, and therefore our sample, could have arisen in the bulk represented by the straight-line graph.

A probability greater than 0·10 and smaller than 0·90, or something between 10 per cent. and 90 per cent., is required to support our assumption. In our case, $\chi^2 = 4·31$, $n = 6$, and we read P as somewhat greater than 0·60, which means that such deviations as we have encountered between our sample frequencies and the corresponding theoretical ones could have arisen about 60 times in 100. We have thus no reason to abandon our assumption, and can regard the theoretical straight line as a satisfactory representation of a bulk showing the same M and σ as our sample.

If a χ^2-table is not available—it was not included in our Appendices in order not to swell the number of Appendices inordinately—we can make use of the relation between the χ^2-function and the Poisson Summation series (see Chapter VI) and read P from the chart, Appendix VB. We enter the chart with $\frac{\chi^2}{2}$ as the mean value (on the horizontal scale) and with $\frac{n}{2}$ as c (the ordinal number of the curves which run across the chart), and read P on the left-hand scale.* In our example, we enter the chart with $m = 2.15$ and $c = 3$, counting 0 as the first term in the partial summation series, and find P somewhat greater than ·60, which is in good conformity with our first value of P.

It should, however, be noted that for practical purposes we seldom go to the trouble of constructing the theoretical graph for our assembly of points and testing by the χ^2-method. Free-hand fitting of a straight line to our distribution is quite admissible, and will in the majority of cases serve our purpose.

3.6 The Distinction Between Bulk (Population) and Sample Quality (II)

We now come to the second part of the problem. It was stated above that what we desired to obtain by the probability graph method was, in principle, the same as what we get by the Quality Control method, viz. an estimate of the bulk from the quality of the samples. As yet, however, our probability graph represents only the bulk as judged from one sample, that is, a bulk having the same M and σ as that sample, although this was a much bigger sample than we had formerly taken in Quality Control work. What is the relation of that picture of the bulk to the " true " bulk in which we are finally interested ?

* This obviously applies only for even n

Let us imagine a bulk of articles containing a very great number, say several millions, of individual articles, then it is evident that if we pick a number of samples of 100 from that bulk we shall get samples whose means and standard deviations differ slightly from sample to sample, and also from the bulk M and σ. It follows that, not only have the individual articles a frequency distribution, but the sample means and sample standard deviations as well, and consequently that we shall get a slightly different estimate of the bulk quality from each of these samples. We know already from paragraph 2.7 that the distribution of sample means is in its form like that of the individuals, and that its standard deviation $\sigma_A = \dfrac{\sigma_B}{\sqrt{n}}$. For the distribution of the standard deviation the formula is more complicated. Provided the sample is great, we can take it as being given by $\sigma_{S.D.} = \dfrac{\sigma_B}{\sqrt{2n}}$.

If n is sufficiently great it is evident that, although the line representing our sample cannot be assumed to be exactly that representing the bulk, yet it will not be very far from it. Utilizing the information of the distribution of means and standard deviations embodied in the above formulae, we can fence off, so to speak, on either side of our cumulative line, an area within which the line representing the bulk may be safely expected to lie, and conversely, if the true bulk line was given, the area in which the lines derived from samples of a certain size might be expected to lie. This is done in the following diagram (3.4). We draw lines L_1, L_2 on each side, parallel to our sample distribution line L, with means $M \pm \dfrac{3\sigma}{\sqrt{n}}$, representing samples of n with the same standard deviation as our original sample, but whose means are the extreme values still compatible with the assumption that they are coming from the same bulk as the original sample.

We then measure on either side of M on the horizontal scale $\sigma \pm \dfrac{3\sigma}{\sqrt{2n}}$, erect vertical lines at these points, find the crossing-points with the horizontal lines drawn at the 16·5 and

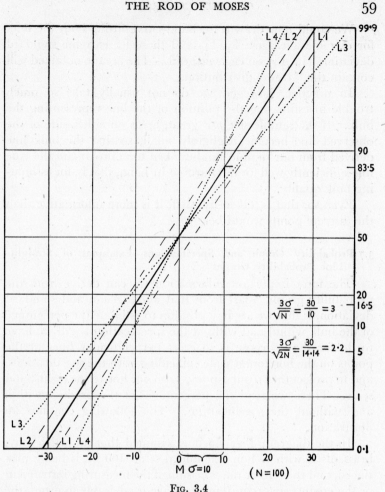

FIG. 3.4

Probability Graph of Sampling Distribution for Mean and σ

83·5 per cent. levels and connect the points so obtained with the centre of L (L_3, L_4). These lines represent samples of n, having the same mean as our original sample, but whose standard deviations are the extreme values still compatible with the assumption that they are coming from the same bulk as the original sample.*

* The construction of such lines is due to a suggestion by Mr. A. Blackwell Ministry of Supply

We could now draw a freehand curve fitting both the lines for extreme averages (L_1, L_2) and those for extreme standard deviations (L_3, L_4) on each side of L. The area so obtained will contain the " true " distribution.

In practice, however, we do not usually take so much trouble in estimating the position of the line representing the bulk. If the sample size n is great, areas on either side of the observed line become negligibly small, so that the bulk line derived from our sample can be taken to approximate the true line sufficiently well for the purpose in hand, that is, for estimating bulk quality.

Even so, that is, taken by itself, it is more informative than the discrete points would be.

3.7 Probability Graph and Specifications—Examples of Straight-Line Probability Graphs

The most important information we can derive from the probability graph, apart from that about mean and standard deviation, is that we are in a position to estimate the percentage of the bulk within and without the specifications. All we have to do for that purpose is to erect perpendicular lines at the points on the horizontal scale coinciding with the specifications, and to project the crossing-points with our line to the right-hand scale. There we read the percentages of the product within and without the specifications. The following contains an illustration.

In the diagram Fig. 3.5 it is assumed that an article, say, brass discs, with a nominal thickness of ·100 in. is being produced, and that either the precision of the measuring instrument or the engineering requirements make it advisable to group the measurements in intervals of ·5 thousandth (·0005) of an inch. Accordingly, the horizontal scale at the bottom of the graph is in ·5 thousandth of an inch. We now plot the cumulative percentage series by putting a dot on the graph wherever the perpendicular erected at the value of a class interval limit crosses the horizontal drawn on the corresponding percentage.

We thus get a distribution of points which will in a great many cases be satisfactorily fitted by a straight line. Let us assume that in a given case such fitting by a straight line is

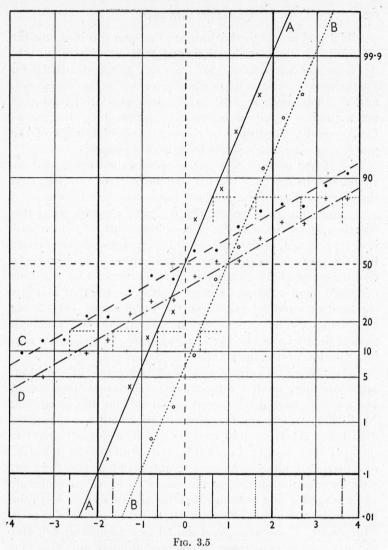

Fig. 3.5

Typical Straight-Line Probability Graphs

A Line of controlled dimension : specification line (0 per cent. outside specification).

B Level of dimension too high by 2 intervals of measurement. Spread as before (5 per cent. outside specification).

C Level of dimension as demanded by specification. Spread has increased (46 per cent. outside specification).

D Level of dimension too high. Spread has increased (48 per cent. outside specification).

possible, and let us further assume that the specifications for the product under consideration are ± 2 thousandths of an inch. At these specification values we erect perpendicular lines. Furthermore, we draw horizontal lines at the points 1 per cent. and 99·9 per cent., because in practical work we hardly ever get a perfect curve asymptotically approaching the *x*-axis. Consequently, the upper and lower horizontal strips of the graph paper are not suitable for practical purposes.

(*a*) If our product was just as specification demanded we would obtain line A. We see that no part of this line, and therefore nothing of the product, lies outside specifications.

Considering that we are dealing with a symmetrical distribution, it follows that the peak should be at the centre, that is at 50 per cent. of the number of observations. We therefore find the mean of the characteristic in question by projecting the crossing-point of the horizontal at 50 per cent. with the Line of Distribution on to the bottom scale. We see that it is just the level required by specifications. Furthermore, considering that the area of the curve *within* the standard deviation on both sides of the mean will be to the area *without* as 2 : 1, we are now in a position to find the standard deviation graphically.

The ratio 2 : 1 corresponds to 67 per cent. : 33 per cent. approximately. Sixty-seven per cent. of the observations should be inside ± once the standard deviation from the mean, and M ± 33·5 per cent. will thus give a clue for finding the standard deviation. As M is at 50 per cent., M ± 33·5 corresponds to 83·5 per cent. and 16·5 per cent., and we obtain the standard deviation by finding the crossing-point of 16·5 or 83·5 per cent. with our distribution line, projecting it on to the bottom scale of the variable and reading there the distance from M to the point so determined.* This gives nearly ·7 thousandth of an inch. Multiplying this amount by 6 should (see paragraph 2.6) give the total range. The range so obtained approximates that laid down by specifications since the total range within specifications is 4 thousandths of an inch, and $6 \times ·7 = 4·2$.

(*b*) Let us assume that we had obtained line B repre-

---

* Conversely, having calculated M and σ, we can immediately construct the straight line with the given M and σ

senting our cumulative curve. We see that part of the product will be outside specification. The percentage of the product outside specification is given by projecting the crossing-point of line B with the upper specification line towards the right. We read 95 per cent. approximately " within," 5 per cent. above specification, and nothing below specification. This indicates that the level of the product has changed. We can make certain about this by projecting the crossing-point of our line with the horizontal at 50 per cent. downwards, and find that the mean has changed by 1/1000 in. The average dimensions of our product will therefore be ·101 instead of ·100.

Constructing the standard deviation as in the former case, we find that it has remained unchanged.

Looking at the graph we see at a glance how to infer a change in the level of production, but stability as far as range of variation goes. In such a case the line will be parallel to the original one representing a product completely within specification, but shifted towards either right or left.

(c) Let us assume that our cumulative curve is adequately represented by line C. We see at a glance again that part of the product will be outside specifications. Applying the same method as above, we read that about 23 per cent. will be above and 23 per cent. below specifications. Constructing the mean, we find that the mean, and therefore the level of production, is exactly as required. Constructing the standard deviation, we find that a considerable change has occurred, as the standard deviation is now 2·5 thousandths of an inch as compared with ·7 thousandth before. The line has not changed its position compared with line A, but its direction is different, and it is such a change in direction—without a change in position—which indicates an increase, or generally a change, in the variability of the product.

(d) If line D represented our sample, we could at a glance infer both change of mean and change of standard deviation, because line D is shifted towards the right, and is no longer parallel to line A. This is confirmed by constructing the mean and standard deviation for this line. We find the mean at 1 instead of at 0, and the standard deviation is 2·6 thousandths instead of ·7 thousandth.

3.8 The Translation of the Geometrical Properties of Probability Graphs into Physical Terms

This short discussion of some of the characteristic differences in probability graphs gives an indication of how to translate the geometrical picture into physical terms. Having a line of comparison such as line A for a sample that meets specifications fully, and plotting lines for the samples actually measured, we can, from a change in the geometrical picture, arrive at an approximate idea of the cause of disturbance (due to assignable causes in the economic sense of the word). A change in position without a change in direction would indicate that the level of the product had changed but not its variability, and therefore that something had gone wrong with the setting of the machine. A change in direction without a change in position would indicate that although the level of production was correct, the variability of the machine was too great, and that matters should be investigated with a view to finding out whether machine tools have become worn, parts of the machine loose, or whether there was too much variability in the operation itself.

If a sample was represented by a line which appeared shifted compared with the standard line, and also had a different direction, we would have an indication that both the setting and the variability of the machine were at fault and required investigation.

3.9 Typical Non-straight Line Probability Graphs

What has been said about probability graphs so far may have given the impression that the points of the cumulative curve will always plot to a straight line on probability paper. But this is by no means the case. The question now arises how to interpret the various typical shapes of graphs. The following paragraphs are a short guide to the correct interpretation of probability graphs.

They should enable the reader to differentiate between the various shapes of graphs, and to draw conclusions from them about the quality of the product yielding such graphs. It should, however, be kept in mind that here, as in every branch of practical work, statistics are not meant to replace but only to supplement common sense, and we must not suppose that a graphical method like the probability graph method is capable of performing wonders.

As has been stressed throughout the " Guide," the method is not primarily meant to provide definite information about the manufacturing *process* of the articles under inspection, though valuable hints as to that process are certainly derivable from it. What we are primarily interested in when applying the method of probability graphs of the Normal Law type is the percentage of the product within the specified limits laid down for the characteristic in question.

(1) Form the cumulative curve and plot on Arithmetic Probability Paper (A.P.P.) according to the instructions given in 3.3. Do not omit to shift the cumulative series upwards by one-half of an interval.

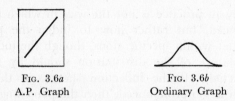

FIG. 3.6*a*   FIG. 3.6*b*
A.P. Graph   Ordinary Graph

(2) If the points plot fairly well to a straight line, read the percentage of the product within specification from the percentage scale on the graph. The decision as to what is a " fairly good " fit must be left to the statistical tact of the investigator. Such tact will be acquired by experience.* The type of curve that will plot to a straight line approximately on A.P. paper is the well-known bell-shaped normal curve.

Be it observed, however, that the conformity of a distribution with the requirements of the normal curve does not say anything about the distribution being a " simple " one. By this is meant that it does not imply that the manufacturing process was controlled in all its parts around one and the same mean, and with one and the same degree of dispersion. The normal distributions which we meet

* As an alternative, the χ^2-test may be applied

with in industrial work will be more often the result of a great number of distributions around different means.

(3) A diagram of this kind results from a distribution curve with more than one mode or peak.

Observe that the inflection (double bend) is in its first part clockwise and in its second counter-clockwise. Such a curve is often the result of the mixing of a number of distributions around different means. What interests us

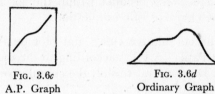

FIG. 3.6c
A.P. Graph

FIG. 3.6d
Ordinary Graph

chiefly in practice is not the way in which the curve was produced, but rather how to judge the percentage of product within specifications, though the indications as to the nature of the distribution should by no means be neglected. If the inflection shown on the probability graph is too pronounced, then the percentage scale of the A.P. paper should not be used.

We can, however, by other means arrive at an estimate of the frequency within certain limits. The method is as follows :

Calculate the standard deviation and divide the distance between tolerance and specification mean by the standard deviation. This gives a quantity " t." We then have

$P \geqslant 1 - \dfrac{1}{t^2}$. This formula, known as Tschebycheff Inequality, means that the percentage of the product lying within specifications will be at least equal to $1 - \dfrac{1}{t^2}$. Con-

sequently, $1 - P$ or $1/t^2$ will give the maximum percentage of pieces outside specifications, as judged from the sample in hand, for a bulk having the same mean and standard deviation as our sample.

What this amounts to is that whatever the form of the distribution, the proportion of the product deviating from the mean by more than

2σ is less than 1/4
3σ is less than 1/9
4σ is less than 1/16.

A determination of this kind will in the majority of cases of examination of components be found to give a sufficiently close estimate of the quality, because the purpose of the examination is not to determine the exact percentage of defects in the bulk, but to spot any unusually bad lot of components.

(4) A curve of this kind results from a symmetrical one-peaked distribution curve, whose central ordinate (height) is greater than it should be according to the Error Function. Observe the characteristic difference between the inflection in this case and that of curve type (3).*   Here the first part

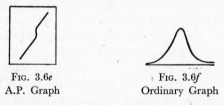

FIG. 3.6e
A.P. Graph

FIG. 3.6f
Ordinary Graph

of the double bend is counter-clockwise and the second clockwise. Such a curve is often the result of a mixture of a number of normal distributions around the same mean but with varying standard deviations. But just as with the type of curve given under (3), it need not be. It can be conceived as representing a distribution function, according to which frequencies of the central values are excessive.

In such a case we again cannot employ the percentage scale of our A.P. paper for estimating the part of the product within and without specified limits. But a formula, similar to that given under (3), allows an even closer guess at the percentage of the population lying within such limits. Calculate the standard deviation and express the distance

* To this fact attention has been drawn by Mr. E. H. Sealy, formerly Ministry of Supply

of tolerance minus specification mean as a multiple of the standard deviation. This gives a quantity " t." Then we have $P \geqslant 1 - \dfrac{1}{2 \cdot 25 t^2}$. This formula is known as the Camp-Meidell Inequality, and the meaning is analogous to that explained under (3). It gives the minimum percentage of the product that can be expected to lie within specifications, and, therefore $\dfrac{1}{2 \cdot 25 t^2}$ represents the maximum percentage outside specifications, for a bulk having the same mean and standard deviation as our sample.

(5) A curve of this kind results from a symmetrical one-peaked distribution in which the frequencies towards the extreme end of the distribution are greater than they should be according to the error function. The type of curve leading to such a graph is shown below. The characteristic of the distribution is that it is deficient in height for values between central and extreme values compared with a normal distribution, and such a deficiency may be caused by any tendency in the process towards depleting the number of values between medium and extreme values beyond the percentage provided for such values by the error function. If the S-shape on the A.P. graph is too pronounced we ought not to use the percentage scale of the A.P. paper for estimating the quality of the lot, but apply the same method and formula as given under (4). The properties of the curves of types 3 and 5 are often

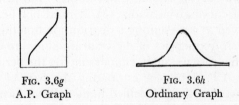

Fig. 3.6g
A.P. Graph

Fig. 3.6h
Ordinary Graph

found to combine and then constitute what is known as " leptokurtic " (narrow humped) curves. In fact, the two graphs on probability paper are clearly seen to be only the extreme forms of one and the same type of inflection.

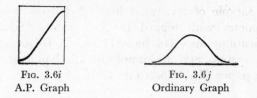

FIG. 3.6*i*
A.P. Graph

FIG. 3.6*j*
Ordinary Graph

(6) A curve of this type results from a one-peaked symmetrical
distribution, in which the values about half-way between
mean and extreme ends are relatively too frequent, taking
the error function as a standard comparison. It may result from a mixture of normal distributions, but it may also
be a homogeneous distribution. If the inverted S-shape
of the graph is too pronounced, the same method as
given under (4) is to be used for estimating the percentage
of the product within specification tolerances.

The properties of curve type 4 and 6 are often found to
combine and then constitute what is known as the " platy-
kurtic " (broad humped) curves. In fact, the two graphs
on probability paper are clearly seen to be only the extreme
forms of one and the same type of inflection.

3.10 Logarithmic Probability Graphs

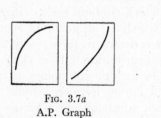

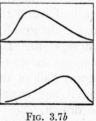

FIG. 3.7*a*
A.P. Graph

FIG. 3.7*b*
Ordinary Graph

If the graph represents a simple curve, either concave or
convex to the horizontal, Logarithmic Probability Paper
(L.P.P.) should be applied for judging the percentage of
the product within specified limits. In order to understand what happens in this case, and what the logarithmic
transformation means, let us consider the following illustration.

A sample of 200 small brass shells was measured with a micrometer with regard to their external diameter whose specifications are ·316 in.–·317 in. A frequency distribution was drawn up, and the cumulative curve plotted on probability graph paper (Table 3.2, Fig. 3.8).

TABLE 3.2

Spec. Mean = ·3165   Spec. Limits ±·0005

Dimension	No. of samples	Cum. curve	Cum. %	Dimension	No. of samples	Cum. curve	Cum. %
·31575	1			·317375		191	95·5
·315875		1	·5	·31750	6		
·316	34			·317625		197	98·5
·316125		35	17·5	·31775	—		
·31625	8			·317875		197	98·5
·316375		43	21·5	·318	2		
·31650	116			·318125		199	99·5
·316625		159	79·5	·31825	—		
·316755	8			·318375		199	99·5
·316875		167	83·5	·31850	—		
·317	24			·318625		199	99·5
·317125		191	95·5	·31875	1		
·31725	—			·318875		200·0	100

According to that determination 5 per cent. of the lot are assumed to lie beyond the upper limit of ·317.

Looking at the graph, which contains the specification lines and the straight line L_1 which is supposed to represent the distribution, we see that it is drawn in such a way as to leave out the upper tail of the distribution. It is clear from the graph that if one wants to include all points, a curve (L_2) should be drawn. Such a curve, however, would not serve our purpose as it would not admit of any inference as to the percentage in the bulk inside and outside specification limits.

The shape of the distribution, in conjunction with what is known about the particular process by which these shells are produced, points to logarithmic probability graph paper as the proper kind of probability graph to use.

The considerations are briefly these. The shells are drawn out by means of a die in continuous production. If that die, at the beginning of the manufacture of the lot, was made

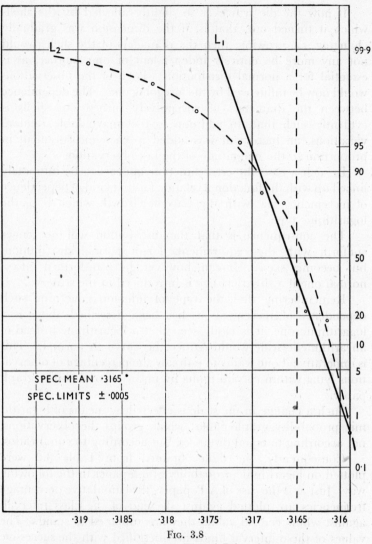

Fig. 3.8

Probability Graph where the Plotted Points follow a Curve

precisely to the correct diameter, it will change ever so slightly from one shell to another until the deviation from the nominal value of the diameter becomes perceptible to the sensitivity of the micrometer.

If now the die was ever so slightly affected by the shells which it turned out, that is, if the dimension was gradually changing, *i.e.* growing, then the diameters of the shells would not any more be entirely independent of one another, as is essential for a normal distribution. Each of the observations would now be influenced by the foregoing one. The dependence between the diameters of successively turned out shells is evidently such that, in addition to the unavoidable random variations, an increment was added to each measurement in proportion to the magnitude of the last observation.

In such a case the error function appears to be intimately linked up with the functional relation for that kind of dependence of increments, viz. with the Law of Growth which is of the logarithmic type.

The consequence is that the distribution will no longer conform with the requirements for a normal distribution, but becomes skew. It can, however, be transformed into a normal one if a slight change is introduced in the scale.*

Remembering that the type of function governing such dependence of increments as has been described above is a logarithmic one, it is easily seen that a logarithmic instead of an arithmetic scale would reduce the curve to normal. This is imperative if one wants to estimate the percentage of observations lying within certain limits by means of probability graph paper.

Such a change in the scale is effected by means of logarithmic probability graph paper, which groups the observations, not according to equal distances, but according to equal ratios.

Consequently, the data obtained from Table 3.2 were plotted on logarithmic probability graph paper in the following way. Just as is the case of A.P. paper, the cumulative percentage frequencies are plotted against the end of the class interval, against whose central values they are supposed to stand. The values of these interval limits are identified with the successive numbers of the logarithmic scale given on the logarithmic graph

---

* Distributions of this kind have been studied by Sir F. Galton and McAlister, *Proc. Roy. Soc.*, vol. 29, 1879, pp. 365, 367 ; G. Th. Fechner, *Kollektivmasslehre*, Leipsic, 1897 ; J. C. Kapteyn, *Skew Frequency Curves in Biology and Statistics*, Groningen, 1903.

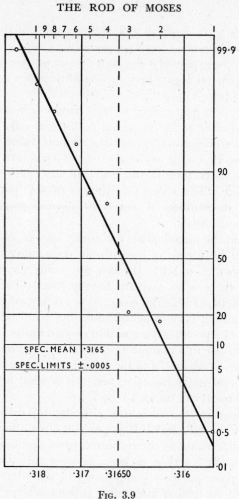

FIG. 3.9
Logarithmic Probability Graph

paper (the long side of the graph rectangle being taken as the basis).

It should be remembered that the effect of using a logarithmic scale is to open the steeper part of the skewed curve, and to push the more gently sloping part together. Consequently, if the steeper part happens to be towards the lower values of the variable, the scale should ascend from the bottom of the graph ;

if it happens to be towards the higher values of the variable, the scale should ascend in the opposite direction.

As was to be expected if the above assumptions were correct, the points plot on logarithmic probability paper satisfactorily as a straight line (Fig. 3.9).

The practical importance of the change in method is that, whereas according to the graph on A.P. paper only 5 per cent. of the measurements are above the critical value of ·317, it appears now that approximately 10 per cent. are above this value. The correctness of this estimate was confirmed from a bigger sample. This shows that the use of A.P. paper in cases where the distribution is far from normal might lead to erroneous conclusions.

It should be noted that the mere fact of obtaining an empirical fit by means of logarithmic probability paper is no strict evidence as to what the law governing the distribution is like, but there is no need for having strict evidence on this point in practical industrial work. We are not concerned here with ascertaining laws of distribution, but with estimating the percentage of a product lying within certain limits. Whenever, therefore, we are in a position to reduce by a legitimate method a skew curve to normal, and the cumulative curve to a straight line, we should make use of it, and this is what a logarithmic probability mesh can do for us.

It is important to realize that although the different shapes of the curve on A.P. and L.P. paper will often allow a guess as to the possible cause of the deviation from normality, it is not this that chiefly interests us here, because the manufacturing process of piece-parts or components is, considered from the viewpoint of the further assembling process, a thing of the past, and because any opinion about the otherwise unknown manufacturing process can only be of a tentative nature. We are more concerned with estimating the quality of the product in order to ascertain whether or not it is fit to go into further production.

The fact we want to ascertain is, therefore, the percentage of the product within specified limits for a given characteristic.

In brief, what matters chiefly is not whether the manufacturing process to which we owe the components was under statistical, but whether it was under economic control.

CHAPTER IV

THE SLIDE RULE PRINCIPLE OF PROBABILITY —THE ANALYSIS OF VARIANCE

4.1 The Necessity for a More Powerful Method of Analysis

UP to now we have learned how to ascertain statistically the presence or otherwise of certain causes of variation in the quality of industrial products (assignable causes), but our methods so far gave no clue as to the extent or amount or intensity of such causes. In order to obtain numerical estimates of the effect of individual causes we must employ other more powerful methods. One of these is called the Analysis of Variance, because it is possible by means of that method to split the combined effect of a number of assignable causes plus random variations into the parts which are due to the various contributions, and so disentangle the contributing factors quantitatively.

As an easy way of approach to the method of analysis of variance I shall choose the control chart method which, as we shall see, is in itself a sort of analysis of variance. I believe that this way of approach will go far to dispel any apprehension as to the large amount of higher mathematics needed for the understanding of the analysis of variance.

4.2 Quality Control Charts as a Simplified Analysis of Variance

Let us assume that an article is produced on a five-spindle automatic in three shifts, that samples of 10 are taken at regular intervals, and that the article is measured for a certain characteristic, say, diameter. In order to set up a quality control chart we calculate the average range of a sufficient number of samples of $10\overline{w}$, multiply with the factor which transforms it into the standard deviation of the population, divide by $\sqrt{n}$ and multiply by 3·09.

The reason for the two last-mentioned operations is this: as we are plotting averages of 10, we want control lines for these averages ; and the ratio in which the standard deviation of the population is reduced in the case of averages is $1/\sqrt{n}$. We thus obtain the standard deviation of the distribution of averages, and multiplying this quantity by 3·09 gives the position of the 1/1000 control lines within which practically all the averages should lie. A simpler but equivalent way is to multiply $\bar{w}_n$ by $A'_{.001}$.

(a) Let us first assume that the five spindles and the three shifts all produce practically the same quality of our article with regard to the characteristic in question. This means that all the samples of 10 which we obtain in a given period of time will be very much alike though not precisely the same. As far as they differ, this could be accounted for by mere chance or, as it is also called, " fluctuations of sampling." In such a case the sample means will themselves be distributed more or less normally around the true mean with a standard deviation amounting to the standard deviation of the population, σ, divided by $\sqrt{n}$ (standard error).

As the quality control chart limits are 3·09 times that quantity on either side of the mean, it follows that if the samples of 10 are only distinguishable from one another by sampling fluctuations, practically all the averages should fall within our control lines.

A Quality Control Chart of that kind therefore represents samples from one and the same population.

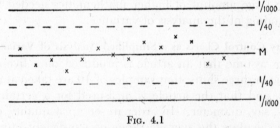

FIG. 4.1

Control Chart showing Process under Control

(b) Now let us assume that the different spindles are set slightly differently so that the level or averages of the dimension in question will not be the same for all the spindles. In such a case, samples of 10 coming from different spindles will be on the whole around different means. The spindle means themselves will again have a distribution, but their standard deviation will now be made up of two parts. First of all there will be a part representing the standard deviation of sample means of 10 coming from one and the same spindle ; that part will be $\dfrac{\bar{\sigma}_s}{\sqrt{10}}$, * where $\bar{\sigma}_s$ is the average standard deviation in samples of 10 specimens.

The second part will not be due any more to sampling fluctuations but to the real differences between the sample means, and will be called σ_a.

The standard deviation of the averages of spindles will therefore be made up of σ_a and $\dfrac{\bar{\sigma}_s}{\sqrt{10}}$. It is actually the squares of these quantities which are additive, but for the moment the relation given above will do.

Now it is clear that, as the control limits are calculated from the range of the samples of 10, there need not be a change in the position of control limits in this case, provided that the variation inside the samples of 10 remains more or less stable regardless from which spindles the samples are taken.

But the picture of the Quality Control Chart with the average points plotted is now very different from what it was before. A number of points will now fall outside the control limits because the variation of averages is now increased by the term σ_a. It depends on the amount of this factor and thus on the amount of difference between the various spindles to what extent the control will be disturbed.

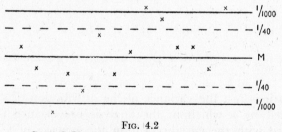

Fig. 4.2
Control Chart showing Process out of Control

* Strictly speaking, σ_s should be corrected for sample size if it is to serve as an estimate of the population standard deviation, but this point is taken care of by the analysis of variance method.

4.3 Deriving the Quantities which are to be compared According to the Analysis of Variance Method

In order to make the transition from the control chart method to the method of analysis of variance—which is nothing new in principle, but gives a very practical arrangement of the arithmetic—it is important to realize that if the standard deviation of the averages in a distribution under control was multiplied by $\sqrt{n}$, it should be equal to the standard deviation in the population :

$$\sigma_{\text{Averages}} = \frac{\sigma \text{ Population}}{\sqrt{n}}$$

therefore $\sigma_A \sqrt{n} = \sigma_P$.

If, on the other hand, the production was not under control and the picture presented by the control chart was that referred to above (*b*), then multiplying the expression :

$$\sigma_a + \frac{\overline{\sigma}_s}{\sqrt{n}}$$

by $\sqrt{n}$ would give

$$\sigma_a \sqrt{n} + \overline{\sigma}_s$$

$\overline{\sigma}_s$ here stands for the average standard deviation within a sample of n, and serves with a certain correction for sample size as an estimate of the standard deviation in the population, σ_P.

It should be noted that in the analysis of variance we use instead of the standard deviations their squares, which are called variances (var), and the relations referred to above then become :

$$\sigma_A{}^2 = \frac{\sigma_P{}^2}{n} \ ; \ \ \therefore n\sigma_A{}^2 = \sigma_P{}^2 \quad . \quad . \quad . \quad . \quad . \quad (4.1)$$

$$\text{var}_A = \sigma_a{}^2 + \frac{\overline{\sigma}_s{}^2}{n} \ ; \ \ \therefore n\text{var}_A = n\sigma_a{}^2 + \overline{\sigma}_s{}^2 \quad . \quad . \quad (4.2)$$

Now it is just the variance of the distribution of averages multiplied by n which in the analysis of variance is being compared with the variance within the samples of n serving as an estimate of σ_P.

The principle, which from the explanation given above is quite evident, is simply this : if n times the variance of the averages approximates the variance within the samples of n, then there is no assignable difference between the samples — $n\sigma_a{}^2$ being sensibly zero—and the samples of n can be considered to come from one and the same population, which is equivalent to saying in quality control work that the process can be considered to be under control. The picture represented by the chart would be one of all the averages falling within the control lines.

If on the other hand the variance of the sample means times n (or $n\mathrm{var}_A$) is significantly different from that within the samples of n, $(\bar{\sigma}_s{}^2)$, the inference is that the samples come from different populations or, as we say in quality control work, that the process is not under control. The picture represented by the quality control chart would be one of a great number of averages falling outside the control lines. By significantly different populations is simply meant that the differences between the sample means are greater than can be accounted for by sampling fluctuations.

In symbols we express the principle of the method of analysis of variance as follows :

Var. of Sample Means . . $n\mathrm{var}_1 \longrightarrow n\sigma_a{}^2 + \bar{\sigma}_s{}^2$
Var. within Samples . . . $\mathrm{var}_2 \longrightarrow \bar{\sigma}_s{}^2$

The question of whether the difference between the variances is significant is decided by calculating the ratio of the variances and reading from certain tables (see Appendix X) the probability that such a ratio could arise by mere chance. If that probability is very small, the criterion of smallness being usually less than 5 per cent., the difference is considered significant. If it is more than 5 per cent. it is considered insignificant. In the first case we would for our example conclude that the spindles are differently set. In the second we would conclude that the setting is, on the whole, on the same level (see Chapter VII, and the following paragraph 4.4, for a fuller explanation of the concept of significance).

To summarize : if everything was completely random or the process completely under control, then the variance *between* samples times n should not be significantly different from that *within* samples, and as each represents an independent estimate of the variance of the total, the latter should not differ significantly from either of the former.

On the other hand, a significant difference of the variance *between* from that *within* samples (the latter being called the " Residual "), which again implies a difference between either or both of these variances and that of the total, denotes a departure from control, or, what amounts to much the same thing, the presence of statistically different populations.

In a similar way, as differences between the spindles might have an effect upon the variability of the product, so the different shifts might have an effect. Applying the same method as before, we should, if the different shifts work all in the same way and produce an article of approximately the same quality, expect that n times the squared standard deviation of the shift means should be approximately the same as that within the samples coming from each shift. If we were to find that this is not the case, and that the standard deviation between the shift means was significantly greater than that within the samples coming from each shift, we would conclude that the changing over from one shift to another implied the introduction of a disturbing factor.

4.4 The Parallelism Between the Two Methods—Statistical Significance

The exact relation between the Analysis of Variance method and that of the Control Chart now becomes clear.

In order to compare two variances, that of sample means and that of the individuals within samples, we must make them comparable. This can be done in two ways. We either multiply the variance of the sample averages by n, and compare it with the variance within samples, or we divide the variance within samples by n, after correcting it for sample size, and compare it with that of the sample averages.

According to which way we choose, we obtain the quantities (mean sums of squares or " variances ") of the analysis of variance, or those of the quality control chart (frequencies of points within and without the control limits).

In symbols we can express the principle of the control chart technique as follows for sufficiently great n :

1/6·18 of the total range of plotted points (averages)

$$\longrightarrow \sqrt{\sigma_a{}^2 + \frac{\overline{\sigma_s}{}^2}{n}}$$

1/6·18 of the distance between 1/1000 control limits $\longrightarrow \dfrac{\overline{\sigma_s}}{\sqrt{n}}$*

If there is no significant difference between the samples, that is, if their averages differ by not more than can be accounted for by fluctuations of random sampling, $\sigma_a{}^2$ will approach zero and the two ranges or distances will be sensibly equal, or, what is the same, all the points will fall within the control limits. Otherwise we say that the process is not under control or is unstable.

The principal features of the Analysis of Variance and the Control Chart technique are thus the same. In both cases the samples of n or the sub-groups are selected in a *non-random* manner with respect to the total population. Both methods now provide tests of very similar mathematical structure for deciding whether the samples behave as random samples from one and the same universe. If they do, the universe is regarded as homogeneous or " under control."

There still remains the question to be answered, What do we mean by saying that variances are, or are not, " significantly different " ?

Supposing the total of the product to be homogeneous in the sense that variations in the characteristic measured are due to nothing but chance causes, then the two values : n var$_1$ (sample means) and var$_2$ (within samples) should be estimates of one and the same quantity, viz. the true variance in the population. Because, however, of unavoidable fluctuations of sampling, they cannot be expected to be exactly equal. The question now arises as to what difference between them can be tolerated without compelling us to conclude that they are estimates not of *one* but of *two different* quantities, and, therefore, point to non-homogeneity of the product ?

We turn again for information to the familiar quality

* To be precise, since we correct the average standard deviation within samples for sample size, this term becomes $\dfrac{\sigma_P}{\sqrt{n}}$

control chart picture. The meaning of the 1/40 limit is that if the scatter of points exceeds these limits in a proportion greater than 2/40—taking both sides together—we have sufficient grounds for suspecting the process to be unstable. As the proportion 2 in 40 corresponds to 5 per cent., these limits represent the values of the variable within which 95 per cent. of the product should lie. The probability of a value beyond is 5 per cent. Such values should thus have a probability of occurrence of 5 per cent. or less if the assumption of homogeneity was to be upheld with confidence. A probability of occurrence of more than 5 per cent. for values beyond these limits would make us suspect that assumption.

Similarly, the probability of a point beyond the 1/1000 limits is—for both sides together—·2 per cent. If the scatter of points is such as to overstep that amount, this is again an indication that the assumption of homogeneity or " control " is to be abandoned. But it should be noted that as we hardly ever have 1000 points on the chart, *any* point falling outside the 1/1000 limits is to be taken as a definite indication that the process has become unstable.

Thus in the control chart technique we compare two values of the measure of dispersion, one obtained from the "within sample variation" (limit lines), and the other from the "between sample variation" (scatter of points), just as we do in the analysis of variance technique.

The occurrence of points beyond the inner or outer limits in a higher than the assigned proportion, implying that there is a probability of more than 5 per cent. or ·2 per cent. respectively of such outliers, is then taken to be incompatible with the assumption of stability or " control."

We can also express this by saying that if the frequency of occurrence of values beyond the 1/40 limits exceeds the 5 per cent. level (or that beyond the 1/1000 limits the ·2 per cent. level), then the assumption of all the samples having come from one and the same universe is no longer justified.

All this is, of course, nothing but a different expression of the familiar rule of the quality control technique, according to which the process is judged to be under control if not more than 1 in 40 points falls outside an inner, and not more than 1 in 1000 beyond an outer limit. Conversely, we conclude that the process has become unstable due to assignable causes if points occur outside these limits in greater than the specified proportions.

Considerations such as these are used wherever the question of " significance " comes up.

The two quantities which in the analysis of variance technique we call " Var. *between* samples " and " Var. *within* samples " should not differ by more than is compatible with their being estimates of one and the same quantity, if we are to be satisfied that the population is homogeneous-random.

The fundamental significance level is taken at 5 per cent. corresponding to our inner control chart limit. If the difference (it is actually the *ratio* which is considered in the analysis of variance technique) is such as could occur at least five times in a hundred in samples of a given size from one and the same universe, then we are satisfied that they are not " significantly different," or that there were no other than random causes active in producing the variability of our product with regard to a certain characteristic. Conversely, if the difference was greater than is compatible with the 5 per cent. level, we conclude that these samples could not have come from one and the same universe.

Instead of the graphical aid provided by the control chart technique for deciding the question of significance, the analysis of variance technique provides us with tables (Fisher's z-tables or those of the Inverted Beta-Function—see Appendix X) from which to read the answer to our question. These tables have sections for different probability levels. Those most often used are the 5 per cent., 1 per cent., ·1 per cent. sections, of which the first corresponds to the level of the inner limits (both sides together) and the last to that of one outer limit.*

The lower the probability level to which the difference between the two variances corresponds, the more confident can we be that the difference is significant. Just as in the control chart technique the overstepping of the inner limits is taken as a warning, whereas that of the outer limits as a

* see Appendix X, which give the three sections in one table

definite indication that the process has become unstable, so in the analysis of variance method the 5 per cent. level represents the border-line between significant and insignificant differences, whereas a difference corresponding to the 1 per cent., or better still the ·1 per cent., level is a very strong indication of non-homogeneity.

4.5 Illustration for Analysis of Variance of Samples Coming from One and the Same Population

The following experiment may serve as an illustration of what has been said in this chapter.

Blue paper discs were stamped out in continuous production to a nominal dimension of their diameter of ·2630 to ·2640 in. These discs were measured by an experienced examiner on a " Travelling Microscope " for diameter.

The first part of the experiment consisted in making the examiner obtain 100 determinations of the diameter of *one and the same disc.* The result was, as expected, an approximately normal distribution of observations. The measurements so obtained were now grouped into samples of 10, in the order in which they were taken, which gives 10 samples of 10 units each. There is no apparent reason why these samples of 10 should differ from one another with regard to their averages and standard deviations by more than can be accounted for by mere chance fluctuations. But there is always the possibility that they do, owing to differences in precision on the part of the examiner from one sample to the next (Table 4.1*a*).

We know from paragraph 4.3 how to test the hypothesis of randomness. We compare *n* times the square of the variance of the sample means with the average variance within the samples. If they are approximately equal we conclude that there is no reason to assume the presence of a disturbing cause, and conversely, if they are significantly different we suspect the presence of such a cause. We thus calculate first the average standard deviation of the samples of 10 and square, and the standard deviation of the sample means, square, and multiply by 10.

The quantities so obtained are then arranged in a form peculiar to the analysis of variance method. Let us recall formula 4·2 where the variance of the total was shown to consist of two parts : variance between sample means and variance within samples. We can write this a little more explicitly :

$$\frac{S(x - \bar{x})^2}{N} = \frac{S(\bar{x}_s - \bar{x})^2}{m} + \frac{SS(x - \bar{x}_s)^2}{nm} \quad . \quad . \quad . \quad . \quad (4.3)$$

where x stands for a measurement, $\bar{x}$ for the average of the total number of measurements (N), $\bar{x}_s$ for a sample average, m for the number of such samples, n for the sample size, S for the operation of summing, and SS for summing first all squared deviations within a sample of n and then summing for all the m samples.

Multiplying through by N, the total number of observations, and considering that $N = nm$, we obtain

$$S(x - \bar{x})^2 = nS(\bar{x}_s - \bar{x})^2 + SS(x - \bar{x}_s)^2 \quad . \quad . \quad . \quad (4.4)$$

That is, we have now expressed the fundamental condition for our analysis in terms of the Sums of Squares instead of squares of standard deviations. The formula (4.4) is for the purpose of the analysis written in table form as follows :

Sources	Sums of squares	Degrees of freedom	Variances
Between rows .	$nS(\bar{x}_s - \bar{x})^2$	$m - 1$	$n\sigma_a^2 + \sigma_s^2$
Residual . .	$SS(x - \bar{x}_s)^2$	$m(n - 1)$	σ_s^2
Total . .	$S(x - \bar{x})^2$	$N - 1$	σ_t^2

where the " degrees of freedom " are nothing but the number of items in each group minus 1, by which the sums of squares are to be divided in order to make us arrive at the *mean sums of squares* or variances which are to be compared for significance.

7

For our experiment the following table resulted (in units of .0001 in.).

TABLE 4.1

Sources	Sums of squares	Degrees of freedom	Variances
Between samples	174	9	19·3
Residual (within samples) .	1724	90	19·1
Total . .	1898	99	19·2

Table 4.1a gives a simplified process of computation.

TABLE 4.1a

To simplify the arithmetic, ·2630 was subtracted from the original measurements, ·2635, ·2641, ·2641, ·2640, ·2644, etc., and the following table resulted.

Sample Number	10 Measurements										Row Totals
1	5	11	11	10	14	12	14	10	9	15	111
2	13	11	16	4	10	8	7	18	15	17	119
3	8	15	7	10	8	8	9	7	10	9	91
4	13	10	11	8	16	15	12	12	9	15	121
5	14	13	2	3	7	11	6	20	7	13	96
6	11	12	11	4	15	3	10	9	12	5	92
7	19	18	7	15	6	8	15	2	13	14	117
8	10	14	9	8	8	9	11	10	8	6	93
9	9	12	17	10	19	15	16	5	18	3	124
10	16	4	13	17	15	9	10	5	17	16	122
											1086

Simplified Process of Computation

(1) Square the Individuals and add :
$$5^2 + 11^2 + 11^2 + \ldots 17^2 + 16^2 = 13692$$

(2) Square the Row Totals and sum, and divide the result by the number of Individuals per row :
$$111^2 + 119^2 + \ldots 124^2 + 122^2 = 119{,}682$$
$$\frac{119{\cdot}682}{10} = 119{\cdot}682$$

(3) Obtain the Grand Total for all Individuals, square and divide by the total Number of Observations :
$$\frac{1086^2}{100} = 11{,}794.$$

Then, if (1), (2), (3) stand for the results of the above operations, equation (4.4) becomes :

$$[(1) - (3)] = [(2) - (3)] + [(1) - (2)],$$

or

$$1898 = 174 + 1724,$$

which quantities now represent the *Sums of Squares* for Total, Rows, and Residual respectively, entered in Table 4.1.

The variances between the samples, within the samples, and of the total are very much alike. This confirms the assumption that there was no difference in operation as regards the examiner's work from one sample of 10 to the next.

In order to satisfy ourselves that the numerical results of the analysis correspond exactly to what was said about its logical foundations, let us determine the relevant quantity, viz. the standard deviation of the sample means, in two ways.

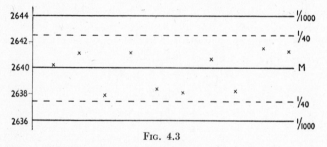

Fig. 4.3

Control Chart for Averages of 10 Measurements taken all on one and the same Disc

First by calculating it as the standard deviation of the means. We obtain for its square as seen in row 1 the value of $19\cdot3/10 = 1\cdot93$. And secondly, according to the formula for the standard error, which, as seen from row 3 gives the value of $19\cdot2/10 = 1\cdot92$ for its square. It is thus the fact that between the sample means there was no greater variation than that due to chance only which made us arrive at the result that there was no disturbing cause present.

Using the graphic method of the quality control chart, we plot the averages of our samples of 10 and draw control limits for the averages whose position we calculate from the range within the samples of 10. Diagram Fig. 4.3 presents the picture of a very satisfactory control.

4.6 Illustration for Analysis of Variance of Samples Coming from Different Populations

In the second part of the experiment 10 different discs were subjected to measurement, and each disc was measured 10 times. We have thus again 100 measurements as in the former case, but this time 10 really different samples of 10 because they represent the measurements taken on 10 different discs.

In this case we should expect that the variation between the samples means to be greater than the variation due only to the standard error of the average of repeated measurements. Arranging the arithmetic again as in the first part of the experiment, viz. first calculating the sums of squares of deviations within the samples, and then calculating the sums of squares of deviations of the sample means and multiplying by n, we obtain the quantities of the second column of the following table (in units of ·0001 in.).

TABLE 4.2

Source of var.	Sums of squares	Degrees of freedom	Variances	Var. ratio
Discs (between samples) .	200	9	22·2	2·06
Within samples (residual) .	970	90	10·8	
Total . .	1170	99	11·8	

The simplified process of computation is shown in Table 4.2a.

TABLE 4.2a

For the purpose of simplifying the arithmetic, ·2630 in. was subtracted from the original measurements, ·2634, ·2635, ·2634, ·2638, etc., and the following table resulted.

Disc. No.	Samples of 10 measurements										Row totals
1	4	5	4	8	7	2	11	2	−1	7	49
2	—	−1	5	18	11	5	4	6	2	2	52
3	—	4	1	4	15	4	5	3	—	2	38
4	11	1	7	14	10	8	10	6	10	4	81
5	3	10	6	10	—	6	5	11	15	5	71
6	1	6	6	5	3	—	8	9	6	6	50
7	3	4	7	5	−2	8	6	5	2	7	45
8	7	6	10	8	9	5	13	4	7	7	76
9	6	1	3	4	2	8	1	6	5	6	42
10	6	9	7	6	1	9	—	6	—	10	54
											558

Simplified Process of Computation

(1) Square the Individuals and sum :
$$4^2 + 5^2 + \ldots 6^2 + 10^2 = 4283.$$

(2) Square the Row Totals and sum, and divide the result by the number of Individuals per row :
$$349^2 + 558^2 + \ldots 228^2 + 430^2 = 33132$$
$$\frac{33132}{10} = 3313 \cdot 2$$

(3) Obtain the Grand Total for all Individuals, square, and divide by the total number of observations :
$$\frac{558^2}{100} = 3113 \cdot 64.$$

Then, if (1), (2), (3) stand for the results of the above operations, equation (4.4) becomes :
$$[(1) - (3)] = [(2) - (3)] + [(1) - (2)]$$
or
$$1170 = 200 + 970$$
which quantities now represent the *Sums of Squares* entered in Table 4.2.

The degrees of freedom are found in the same way as in the former case. We have 10 samples of 10, therefore the mean sum of squares of the sample mean deviations is obtained by dividing through by $10 - 1 = 9$. In a sample of 10 there are $10 - 1$ arbitrary observations, which gives 9 observations. Multiplying this figure by the number of samples we get 90, giving the degrees of freedom for the second row. For the total we have $100 - 1 = 99$, the sum of the degrees of freedom in rows 1 and 2.

The last column contains the variances which are to be compared. We find this time a significant difference between the variance of the means and that within the samples of 10. The ratio between the two is 2·06, for which we read in the tables of the variance ratio,* that a difference such as this between two variances would arise less than 5 times in 100 by chance. We thus conclude that this is due to a real difference between the sample means. The analysis has thus brought out what in this case we knew from the beginning, viz. that there were real differences between the samples of 10.

If we now wanted to obtain the contributions to the total variation by the accidental variation and the real variation between the measurements, we should have to proceed in the following way.

The variance " between " the samples is made up of two parts, viz. 10 times the square of the standard deviation between the discs, plus the residual.

We thus obtain $22\cdot2 = 10\sigma_a^2 + 10\cdot8$, from which $\sigma_a^2 = 1\cdot14$ and $\sigma_a = 1\cdot07$. The standard deviation of the *means* is then made up in the following way :

$$\sigma_D^2 = \sigma_a^2 + \frac{\overline{\sigma_s}^2}{10}$$

therefore, $1\cdot14 + (10\cdot8 \div 10) = 2\cdot22$
the first term showing the contribution of the real, and the second of the chance, variation.

2·22 is the total standard error of the means, due to fluctuations of sampling and the real differences. It is, of course, nothing else but the variance between samples 22·2 divided by the sample size of 10.

On the other hand, the standard deviation of the *total* should also be made up of two parts : the squared standard deviation of discs plus the squared standard deviation within the samples of 10. We obtain from the foregoing :

$$1\cdot14 + 10\cdot8 = 11\cdot94$$

* Appendix X

This is in good harmony with the variance calculated from the total of observations which we find in the last row of our table, namely, 11·8.

In order to represent the foregoing analysis graphically, let us again plot the averages and calculate the control limits for these averages from the sample ranges. The following chart points unmistakably to a lack of control, which would become more pronounced as the observation was prolonged.

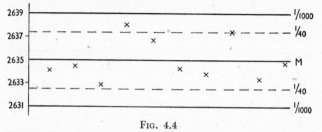

FIG. 4.4

Control Chart for Averages of 10 Measurements, each Sample of 10 taken from a different Disc

4.7 Estimating the Amount of Variance Contributed to the Total Variance by each Component Distribution or Cause—The Slide Rule Principle of Probability

The question now arises as to what use we can make of the results of analysis of variance, apart from discovering whether two samples come from the same population or not. The answer is briefly this—that it allows us to assess the effect of each of the disturbing factors, which is a preliminary for removing them, or if we are not able to do this, for using a corresponding correction in our final estimate of the quality of the work.

The principle I am going to explain now is one of the most important in statistical theory, and at the same time one of the most astonishing.

Let us think of a variable characteristic which is the combined effect of a number of contributing causes. To fix our ideas, let us speak of a certain dimension (diameter) of the article produced on our five-spindle automatic in three shifts. Let us further assume we had established by analysis of variance that into the variation of that dimension there enter the causes of : difference between spindles, difference between shifts, and, of course, random errors. This means that the dimension in question of each individual article will be the result of a combination of the two assignable causes, plus chance causes. As each of the " causes " is a chance variable, that is, a variable which can take on different values with different probability, we must think of three frequency distributions compounded into one. The best description for what happens in such a case is provided by a term sometimes used colloquially in connection with the assembly of two types of components : we say that the components are being " married " to one another.

Now this is precisely what happens to the distributions, if by " marrying " we mean " mating." It is not a question of merely adding the frequencies of a given value of the variables in all three distributions. By no means. Something much more complicated happens. Provided that there is no correlation between the variables, any value of a chance variable can meet with any value of another chance variable. A high value of variable 1 will meet sometimes with a high value of variable 2, but can equally well meet with a low value or a medium value. Even here, among inanimate objects, " mating " is not always " matching." The result of compounding chance variables is thus not a *summing* of frequencies only, but a sort of *multiplication in thought*. Any value of variable 1 has an equal chance of meeting with any value of variable 2, which forcibly reminds one of the inalienable right of the hereditary units, the genes, to combine freely according to the Mendelian Laws of Heredity, which are nothing but Laws of Chance.

But how are we to follow an operation of such complexity between our chance variables, and is it conceivable that we should be able to predict the properties of the resulting compounded distribution ?

The answer is that this has been made possible by a method analogous to that which has made multiplication easy. This, as is well known, has been achieved by means of logarithms. Let me recall the principle of it as it is embodied in the Slide Rule.

If we want to multiply, say, 3 by 4, we set the lower scale so as to make its 1 coincide with the 3 of the upper one and then read off the upper scale the figure 12 which coincides with the

4 on the lower. We have thus merely added two *distances* instead of multiplying 3 by 4, because the scales are logarithmic scales, and two numbers are multiplied by adding their logarithms and raising their " base," 10 as a rule, to a power equalling the sum of their separate logs.

A similar device happens to be available for the compounding of frequency distributions. If we want to obtain the standard deviation of the result of " marrying," that is, *multiplying* in thought, or, which is the same, in a random way, a number of component distributions, all we have to do is to *add* their variances (squares of standard deviations) and take the square root of that sum. We thus obtain the result of a most complicated " multiplication " simply by summing the squares of certain distances epitomizing these distributions.

We know, therefore, that if a number of distributions of independent causes for one and the same characteristic, but which are significantly different in the sense explained above, are compounded into one single distribution, then the standard deviation of that distribution :

$$\sigma_{\text{total}} = \sqrt{\text{sum of variances of component distributions}} \qquad (4.5)$$

In terms of the Theory of Statistics, the theoretical justification for the interpretation given above is as follows (as far as normal distributions are concerned).

The Generating Function $G(t) = \int \phi(x) t^x dx$ is transformed into the Moment Generating Function by putting $t = e^a$. We then obtain

$$G(e^a) = \int \phi(x) e^{ax} dx = 1 + \mu_1^1 a + \mu_2^1 a^2/2! + \mu_3^1 a^3/3! + \ldots$$

The logarithm of that function can be expanded in powers of a in the form $\lambda_1 a + \lambda_2 a^2/2! + \lambda_3 a^3/3! + \ldots$ (seminvariant generating function) where the coefficients λ_i are called the seminvariants of the function $\phi(x)$. Now since moment generating functions, like simple probabilities, are compounded in product, seminvariant generating functions are compounded in sum. Hence the theorem : when independent systems are compounded, the rth seminvariants of the separate systems are added to form the rth seminvariant of the compound system. This is called the additive property of the seminvariants (see Aitken, *Statistical Mathematics*, pp. 21, 22).

Now the second seminvariant is always the square of the standard deviation, and, therefore, by the above theorem the variance of the compound system is equal to the sum of the variances of the component systems.

Further, as for the Normal distribution—and it is more or less Normal distributions which arise in industrial work—all semin-variants beyond the second are zero, and as the origin in all these distributions can be taken at zero, we can conceive of the compounding of independent normal systems as being carried out by adding the logarithmic expressions for these systems and finding the antilogarithm to that sum in the form of the M.G.F. of the compound system.

4.8 Application of this Principle to Industrial Data—Estimating the Amount of Variance Contributed by Divers Engineering Causes

Let us now apply this to the example under consideration. Let us call the standard deviation due to differences in spindles σ_1, that due to shifts or machines σ_2, and that within our samples of 10 σ_3. Furthermore, let us call quite generally the number of spindles n_1, the number of shifts or machines n_2 and the number of articles in a sample n_3. We then have from formula (4.5) the relation

$$\text{Standard deviation of total} = \sqrt{\sigma_1^2 + \sigma_2^2 + \sigma_3^2} \quad . \quad (4.6)$$

The question is now how to estimate the σ's on the right-hand side of the equation. This is easily done if we bear in mind the fundamental principle of the analysis of variance as explained above. Supposing we wanted to know whether there existed a disturbing factor due to spindle differences. We would then calculate the means of the product coming from each spindle, the standard deviation between these spindle means as if they were individual measurements, and multiply its square by n, the number in the sample we were regularly taking. The value so obtained we would then compare with the square of the average of the standard deviations within the samples of n, as described above, and draw our conclusions according to whether these two values are sensibly equal (no disturbing factor) or significantly different (disturbing factor).

The first of these values approaches for very great n

$$v_1 \longrightarrow + n_3 \sigma_1^2 + \bar{\sigma}_3^2$$

the second $\quad v_3 \longrightarrow + \bar{\sigma}_3^2.$

We write this relation in the form of equations $v_1 = n_3 \sigma_1^2 + \bar{\sigma}_3^2$

and $v_3 = \bar{\sigma}_3^2,$

and have from them $\sigma_1^2 = \dfrac{v_1 - \bar{\sigma}_3^2}{n_3} = \dfrac{v_1 - v_3}{n_3} \quad . \quad . \quad (4.7)$

This applies to any number of suspected disturbing factors (shifts, machines, etc.) and puts us into a position to determine the contribution of each disturbing cause, to the total variation in the product. The sum of variances (σ_i^2's) thus obtained, plus the residual representing the variance due to random errors, should then be sensibly equal to the variance of the total, according to formula (4.6). This puts us in a position to describe the relative or percentage amount of contribution by each of these factors to the total variation.

It should be noted, however, that the " variances " of the table of analysis of variance, the " v's," are not additive in the sense that they would add up to the variance of the total, because *each* " variance " there (each v_i) is an independent estimate of the variance of the total, provided that their differences are not significant.

4.9 How Such Information Can be Used for Improving the Method of Control, and, Thereby, for Improving the Quality of the Product

Apart from furnishing important information of that kind, we can turn the results of analysis of variance to good use for the purpose of controlling quality by means of Charts more effectively.

With that end in view, a little transformation of the fundamental formula (4.6) becomes necessary. What interests us in quality control work is sample averages. As we have seen, an average in our example might be affected in three different ways. It might deviate from the true mean because of the effect of the cause " spindle." It might deviate from it as the effect of the cause " shift " or " machine." And it will deviate from the true mean because of random errors or fluctuations of sampling.

What we want to know is the standard deviation we must expect for sample averages which are affected in this threefold way, if the product coming from all machines and spindles is compounded into one total distribution and the sample picked at random.

Using the same symbols as before, we know that the standard error of the spindle means will be : σ_1

that of the distribution of the shift, or machine, means : σ_2 and that due to fluctuations of sampling : $\sigma_3/\sqrt{n_3}$.

As the standard error of the mean is nothing else but the standard deviation of the distribution of means, we obtain the standard error of the compound distribution of means by applying the formula (4.5), inserting in place of the standard deviation σ_3 of the frequency distribution, the standard deviation of the means of *that* distribution, thus :

$$\text{Standard Error of total} = \sqrt{\sigma_1{}^2 + \sigma_2{}^2 + \frac{\sigma_3{}^2}{n_3}} \qquad . \qquad . \qquad (4.8)$$

What use can we make of formula 4.5 and 4.8 in Quality Control work ? Let us first assume that it is feasible to remove the disturbing factors. The engineer, after having been informed of the results of our statistical investigation, might arrive at such a decision. The question now arises as to what to take as a basis for calculating our control lines. Clearly, if we succeed in eliminating the influence of the disturbing factors, we should be able to work to control limits governed by nothing but random errors. The residual, $\sigma_3{}^2$, being the square of the standard deviation of that random error distribution, thus represents the quantity from which to obtain our control limits. (Take square root and multiply by factors given in Appendix IV(*a*) or multiply $\sigma_3/\sqrt{n_3}$ by 1·96 for the 1/40, and by 3·09 for the 1/1000 limit.)

The second possibility is that nothing can be done about removing the disturbing factors. In such a case we must work to somewhat wider limits if we wanted to use our charts as efficient control charts at all.

The limits calculated from the range of our samples of *n* would evidently be too narrow because they leave out the increase in variation due to the influence of the disturbing factors, and would thus give too many points outside. This in turn would necessitate adjusting the machines or spindles very often for causes which, according to the hypothesis, it was impossible to remove. The net result would be that instead of an improvement in the quality of our product, we would only achieve a deterioration. But provided the specifications for our characteristic do not forbid any extension of the range of measurements, we can from formula (4.8) obtain control lines spaced so as to embrace the great majority, if not all, of the averages. What we have to do is to take the standard error of the total as calculated there as the starting-point from which to calculate our control limits. (Multiply the standard error by 1·96 and 3·09 and add or subtract from average of averages.)

4.10 Detection of Variations in Setting

As an illustration for the use of formula 4.8, let us return to the operation discussed in Chapter II, viz. the presswork operation of setting percussion caps to a specified depth. We shall see that formula 4.8 enables us to arrive at a physical interpretation of great practical interest of the difference between the total variance of sample means and the variance from which the control limits are obtained.

If the dimension which is to be controlled depends, as it does in this case, upon the correct setting of the machine, then it is clear that the extent of deviation from the specification mean will depend, not only upon the chance deviations from that mean, but also on the setter's ability to keep close to the specification or drawing average, and on the influence of tool wear which might cause the setting to drift in one direction instead of remaining fixed.

In brief, the settings themselves will have a frequency distribution around the specification mean. This distribution we must imagine to be superimposed upon that of the chance variations of the product around a given setting, the former having its source in the machine plus servicing, the latter in the quality of the components which are to be assembled plus the operation of the machine.

Assuming the setting to remain fairly constant while small samples of, say, five units are taken, which is equivalent to assuming that the range is under control, then the variation *within* such samples transformed into that of the population of sample means according to the formula $\dfrac{\bar{w}_n}{d_n\sqrt{n}}$ will be a good measure of the variability of means due to the quality of components and the operation of the machine. $\dfrac{\bar{w}_n}{d_n\sqrt{n}}$ is, of course, nothing else but the standard error of the mean in a normal population which, multiplied by 1.96 and 3·09, gives our 1/40 and 1/1000 limits respectively. We can also describe it as that part of the standard deviation of means which is due to chance.

Now from paragraph 4.8 we know that according to the slide-rule principle of probability, the total variance of sample means (that is, the square of the standard error of means) equals the sum of the variances of the component distributions of means. In our case (see formula (4.8)).

St. Error^2 (tot.) = St. E.^{2} (chance dev.) + St. E.^{2} (settings) It follows that the difference

$$\text{St. E.}^2 \text{ (tot.)} - \left(\frac{\bar{w}_n}{d_n \sqrt{n}}\right)^2$$

will give the *variance of sample means due to setting* (the range assumed to be under control). This, then, is the physical interpretation of the difference between the total variance of sample means and the variance upon which the control limits are based.

We obtain this quantity either by an analysis of variance calculation of the type carried out above (paragraphs 4.5, 4.6), or directly from the control chart for averages by determining the standard deviation of all the points plotted (for a rough approximation we could divide the total range of plotted points by 6), squaring, and substracting from it the square of 1/6 of the distance between the 1/1000 control limits.

The magnitude of the quantity so obtained, relative to the total variance, is a measure of the extent to which setting variations interfere with the uniformity of our product. If it is considerable, and if the setting variations cannot be reduced satisfactorily, we must allow for them in setting our control limits by increasing the distance due only to chance by an appropriate amount.

To give an idea of the extension of control limits for averages in such cases, it may suffice to say that very often a distance (of the 1/1000 limits from the mean) of four instead of three times the standard deviation of averages will be found necessary for accommodating practically all sample averages.

4.11 Multifactorial Design

In paragraphs 4.5 and 4.6 the analysis of variance method was used for determining the dependence (or otherwise) of a certain effect upon the variation in *one* cause. Very often, however, the question arises of whether a given effect is dependent upon a number of causes, and also, how such causes are interlocked with one another in producing the effect.

The analysis of variance method, although perfectly able to provide a complete answer to problems of this kind—in fact, it is then that it shows its full power—becomes rather complicated in such cases. Performing a difficult analysis without mastery of the analytical relations involved, brings with it the risk that it might degenerate into a mechanical procedure whose working is a mystery to the person applying it.

The difficulties of carrying out a complex, that is multifactorial, analysis are partly due to the usual method of doing the various parts of the analysis as far as possible simultaneously, for the sake of economising in arithmetical labour. Since, however, sacrifice of economy in arithmetical work is preferable to sacrifice of understanding, a slight modification of the original method is set forth in this paragraph, which, *by taking out the effect of one cause at a time*, and thus proceeding step by step in the logical order of what we have made it our aim to achieve, demands at each step nothing more than the simple analysis of variance explained in paragraphs 4.5 and 4.6. It has thus the effect of resolving the multi-variate case into a sequence of univariate ones.

An experiment was carried out with a view to testing the protection against corrosion of steel afforded by coating treatments of the steel (" undercoats ") and paint systems. Five different treatments were given to equal numbers of steel panels, which were further protected by five different systems of paint, the number of panels for each combination of a given treatment with a given paint system being the same. These panels were then subjected to weathering influence (natural or artificial) and, after a certain time, the " amount of corrosion " ascertained, as epitomized by the area and the depth of the corrosion spots occurring on a panel. The " marks " which the panels thus received were averaged for the panels belonging to the same combination of treatment and paint system. In the following Table 4.3, the rows denote the five treatments, the columns the different paint systems, whereas the entries in the body represent the "amounts of corrosion" for each row column combination, in terms of the adopted system for evaluating the results.

TABLE 4.3

Paint system \ Treatment	0	1	2	3	4	Sums	Means
0	25	15	13	16	13	82	16·4
1	20	16	17	13	10	76	15·2
2	19	19	11	13	9	71	14·2
3	18	11	14	11	7	61	12·2
4	11	8	11	4	10	44	8·8
Sums	93	69	66	57	49	334	
Means	18·6	13·8	13·2	11·4	9·8		13·36

We will start with ascertaining whether the differences in the amount of corrosion, as we proceed from one treatment to the next, point to significant differences in those causes, in other words, whether we can rely on certain treatments giving better protection than others.

The following arrangement of the arithmetic is only another expression of that set forth in Table 4.1a, but it is to be recommended in the case of multi-variate analysis because it is less liable to confusion. The steps are :

(1) Form the sum of squares of all entries, namely 4984.
(2) Form the sum of the five products : row sum by row mean, 4639·6 in our case.
(3) Each of these sums must be corrected for transference to the general mean by subtracting the product : total sum by total mean, 4462·24.

This gives the equation (1) − (3) = [(2) − (3)] + [(1) − (2)], or, numerically

$$521·76 = 177·36 + 344·4 \quad \cdots \cdots \quad (4·9)$$

where the first term is the sum of squared deviations from the general mean, the second represents the variation "between" rows, and thus is the sum of the squared deviations of the row-means from the general mean, and the third is the sum of the squared deviations from the row-means, and thus the variation "within" rows.

This represents a partial result which cannot be interpreted in physical terms until the other variable causes which we wish to consider have been dealt with.

In order to ascertain whether we can rely on certain paint systems to give better protection than others, we must now analyse the data with regard to columns.

We first subtract from each entry in Table 4.3 the corresponding row-mean, and obtain the following Table 4.4 :

TABLE 4.4

Paint system \ Treatment	0	1	2	3	4	Sums
0	8·6	− 1·4	− 3·4	− 0·4	− 3·4	0
1	4·8	0·8	1·8	− 2·2	− 5·2	0
2	4·8	4·2	− 3·2	− 1·2	− 5·2	0
3	5·8	− 1·8	1·8	− 1·2	− 5·2	0
4	2·2	− 0·8	2·2	− 4·8	1·2	0
Sums	26·2	2·2	− 0·8	− 9·8	− 17·8	0
Means	5·24	0·44	− 0·16	− 1·96	− 3·56	

We then treat this table in the same way as the original table—that is, we deal with its entries as if they were the original ones—with the only difference that we now determine the variation between *columns* instead of between rows. (Proceed according to the steps given above, substituting "column" for "row." Since the overall mean of Table 4.4 is zero, step three leaves the sums of squares unchanged.)

This leads to the equation

$$344·4 = 220·9 + 123·5 \quad \ldots \ldots \ldots (4.10)$$

Comparing (4.10 with 4.9), we see that what we have done in the second part of our analysis was to resolve the variation " within " or the residual of (4.9) into two parts, viz. the contribution of the column effect and another (reduced) residual.

Combining both equations, we have

$$521 \cdot 76 = 177 \cdot 36 + 220 \cdot 9 + 123 \cdot 5 \quad . \quad . \quad . \quad (4.11)$$

Let A, B, C, D, E, in the following " Latin Square " represent levels of a third cause, say five different types of steel used for the panels :

$$
\begin{array}{ccccc}
A & B & C & D & E \\
E & C & A & B & D \\
B & D & E & C & A \\
D & E & B & A & C \\
C & A & D & E & B \\
\end{array}
$$

Summing and averaging the five entries in Table 4.3 corresponding to each of these letters, we now proceed exactly as if they were row or column sums and averages. We first subtract the column means from the entries in Table 4.4, which gives us a further reduced table to which to apply the simple analysis of variance procedure according to the steps set forth above, substituting " letter-mean or -sum " for row-mean or -sum.

The result would be an equation where the last residual of 123·5 would be split up into the " letter "—that is, the type of steel—contribution and a final residual.

Taking, however, only two causes into account, treatment and paint system, we can now set up the following analysis of variance table from equation (4.11) :

Source	Sums of squares	D. of Fr.	Variance	Prob.
Treatment	177·36	4	44·3	$< \cdot 01$
Paint	220·8	4	55·2	$\leqslant \cdot 01$
Residual	123·5	16	7·7	
Total	521·76	24		

In the last column we see that the differences in the degree of corrosion between panels subjected to either different treatments or different paint systems are such as would occur on pure chance less than once in a hundred. Neglecting such small probabilities, we conclude that the various treatments and paint systems really differ with regard to the degree of protection which they afford against corrosion.

For the reader interested in the mathematical side of the matter I give below the analytical structure of the modified method.

Denoting the single observation possibly depending upon two causes by y_{ij}, each subscript standing for one of those causes, the respective averages by $\bar{y}_i$ and $\bar{y}_j$ and the grand average by $\bar{y}$, the number of rows by h and that of columns by k, we can write for the Standard Deviation squared :

I (a) $\sigma y_{ij}^2 = \dfrac{\Sigma\Sigma(y_{ij} - \bar{y})^2}{N} = \dfrac{\Sigma\Sigma y_{ij}^2}{N} - \left(\dfrac{\Sigma\Sigma y_{ij}}{N}\right)^2$ (See Appendix II)

$$\sigma = N\sigma_{y_{ij}}^2 = \Sigma\Sigma(y_{ij} - \bar{y})^2 = \Sigma\Sigma y_{ij}^2 - \frac{(\Sigma\Sigma y_{ij})^2}{N} \quad . \quad . \quad . \quad (4.12)$$

In words : Total sums of squares = sums of squares of entries Table 4.3 − Prod. (Total Mean by Total Sum).
This represents the combination of Steps 1 and 3.

(b) $\Sigma\Sigma(y_{ij} - \bar{y})^2 = \Sigma\Sigma(y_{ij} - \bar{y}_i)^2 + k\Sigma(\bar{y}_i - \bar{y})^2$
(See equation (4.4))

$$\Sigma\Sigma(y_{ij} - \bar{y})^2 - k\Sigma(\bar{y}_i - \bar{y})^2 = \Sigma\Sigma(v_{ij} - \bar{y}_i)^2 \quad . \quad . \quad . \quad (4.13)$$

Now since

$$\Sigma(\bar{y}_i - \bar{y})^2 = \Sigma\bar{y}_i^2 - \frac{(\Sigma\bar{y}_i)^2}{h} = \Sigma\bar{y}_i^2 - \left(\frac{\Sigma\Sigma y_{ij}}{k}\right)^2 \Big/ h$$

$$k\Sigma(\bar{y}_i - \bar{y})^2 = k\Sigma\bar{y}_i^2 - \frac{(\Sigma\Sigma y_{ij})^2}{kh}$$

$$= \Sigma k\bar{y}_i \cdot \bar{y}_i - \frac{(\Sigma\Sigma y_{ij})^2}{N} \quad . \quad . \quad . \quad . \quad . \quad . \quad . \quad . \quad . \quad (4.14)$$

Letting the letter h stand for the number of rows and k for the number of columns, this means in words :

Sum of squares " between rows " = sum of products (Row Sum by Row Mean) − product (Total Sum by Total Mean).
This represents the combination of Steps 2 and 3.

II According to equation (4.13), subtracting (4.14) from (4.12) is equivalent to forming the quantity $\Sigma\Sigma(y_{ij} - \bar{y}_i)^2$ or the residual. We obtain this quantity numerically from Table 4.3, by subtracting from each entry the corresponding row-mean, squaring, and summing over all entries.

Repeating now for the columns (subscript j) what we have done for rows (I), and remembering that our basic quantities are now the $(y_{ij} - \bar{y}_i)$ differences, we have (h denoting the number of rows) :

$$\Sigma\Sigma(y_{ij} - \bar{y}_i)^2 - h\Sigma(\bar{y}_j - \bar{y})^2 = \Sigma\Sigma(y_{ij} - \bar{y}_i - \bar{y}_j)^2 \quad . \quad . \quad (4.15)$$

$$\text{or} \quad \Sigma\Sigma(y_{ij} - \bar{y}_i)^2 = h\Sigma'(\bar{y}_j - \bar{y})^2 + \Sigma\Sigma(y_{ij} - \bar{y}_i - \bar{y}_j)^2$$

In words :

Sum of Squared Entries (Table 4.4) = Sum of Prod. (Col. Mean by Col. Sum) — (Tot. Sum by Tot. Mean) + Residual. We see that the result of the operation is to reduce the entries in Table 4.4 still further by the corresponding Column Means.

Carrying out Parts I and II simultaneously, we write equation ($4v\sigma$) as

$$\Sigma(y_{ij} - \bar{y})^2 - k\Sigma(\bar{y}_i - \bar{y})^2 - h\Sigma(\bar{y}_i - \bar{y})^2 = \Sigma\Sigma(y_{ij} - \bar{y}_i - \bar{y}_j)^2$$

$$\text{or} \ \Sigma\Sigma y_{ij}^2 - \frac{(\Sigma\Sigma y_{ij})^2}{N} - \left(k\Sigma\bar{y}_i^2 - \frac{(\Sigma\Sigma y_{ij})^2}{N}\right) - \left(h\Sigma\bar{y}_i^2 - \frac{(\Sigma\Sigma y_{ij})^2}{N}\right)$$

$$= \Sigma\Sigma(y_{ij} - \bar{y}_i - \bar{y}_j)^2 \quad . \quad . \quad . \quad . \quad . \quad (4.16)$$

In words :

Sum of Squares — (Total Sum by Total Mean) — [Sum of Prod. (Row Sum by Row Mean) — (Tot. Sum by Tot. Mean)] — [Sum of Prod. (Col. Sum by Col. Mean) — (Tot. Sum by Tot. Mean)] = Residual.

III   The process could now be repeated for a third variable cause, described by a letter subscript L, leading to the equation

$$\Sigma\Sigma\Sigma(y_{ijL} - \bar{y})^2 - k(\bar{y}_i - \bar{y})^2 - h(\bar{y}_j - \bar{y})^2 - l(\bar{y}_L - \bar{y})^2$$
$$= \Sigma\Sigma\Sigma(y_{ijL} - \bar{y}_i - \bar{y}_j - \bar{y}_L)^2 \quad . \quad . \quad . \quad . \quad (4.17)$$

and, indeed, for any number of variables, each step implying a further reduction of the original table. We can thus conceive of each observation as being made up in the following way :

$$y_{ijL} = \bar{y}_i + \bar{y}_j + \bar{y}_L + \text{Residual} \quad . \quad . \quad . \quad . \quad . \quad . \quad (4.18)$$

Chapter V

THE COMPASS OF CHANCE—CORRELATION *

5.1 Trends—The Relation Between Trend and Significant Differences

ALL we have been concerned with hitherto is the distribution of measurements, sample averages, and ranges, of the variable represented by the vertical scale of the quality control chart.

The form of the distribution along the horizontal scale which represents the order of our samples according to the method of sub-grouping did not concern us, or rather was left out of account, except for the brief mentioning of Trends, paragraph 2.12. It is time we devoted some attention to that second aspect of the plotted chart.

It is not a very rare occurrence in practical work to get charts showing the following picture :

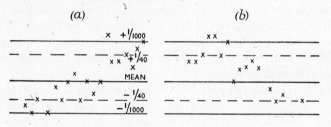

Fig. 5.1

Part of Control Chart for Averages showing Trends

Translating the picture into words, the higher the ordinal number of our sample the greater the value of the average of the sample (a) or vice versa (b).

Clearly this would indicate a departure from randomness. Some regularity has come in which disturbs the free play of chance.

But the assignable cause we meet here acts in a somewhat

---

* For a thorough exposition of the Theory of Correlation, the reader is referred to Chapters 11–16 of the *Introduction to the Theory of Statistics*, G. *Udny Yule* and *M. G. Kendall*, 11th edition, 1937.

different way from that accountable for by a disturbing factor in general.

First, it is only relative to the sub-groups we have chosen that we can speak of lack of randomness. We need not find the disturbance absolutely, that is, without reference to a second qualitatively different variable.

Secondly, it is not only a disturbing factor but one which, although it disturbs randomness, introduces a peculiar kind of regularity and order. As such it admits of a new kind of " control " as we shall see presently.

The ascertaining of a trend on our chart is of just as much importance as that of a state of control, or lack of it, in the usual sense of the term. It is closely connected with the latter because if the trend is allowed to continue it is inevitable that the averages should soon fall outside the control lines, and lack of stability would be the consequence. Charts should, therefore, be closely watched for indications of trend.

If an unmistakable trend occurs, it is a matter for the production engineer (if the sub-grouping was according to a technical criterion, say, different spindles or machines) or the administrative officer (if the sub-grouping was according to a labour criterion, say, shifts) to do everything in his power to eliminate such disturbance.

The relation between our former method for ascertaining disturbing factors—analysis of variance—and this method—trend—can be formulated as follows :

For a trend to arise it is *necessary* that the sample means should differ by more than they are supposed to do if all the samples came from one and the same population. This is also the necessary condition for the presence of a disturbing factor in general or for lack of control.

But whereas such condition is also *sufficient* in the general case, it is not sufficient for the emergence of a real trend. Such a phenomenon arises only if the successive significantly different sample means form, on the whole, an increasing or decreasing series.

In other words, when a disturbing factor is ascertained by analysis of variance, there is not always a trend. But wherever there is a trend there is also a significant result according to analysis of variance, provided the sub-grouping is according to the same variable.

5.2 The Use of Inclined Control Limits

It seems evident that, as a general rule, the variable according to which we sub-group should not be correlated with the characteristic which we wish to control. This is one of the conditions under which we can expect the sample averages to come within the control limits.

But there are conceivable cases in which the only sensible way of sub-grouping is according to a variable which is correlated with the characteristic for which we sample, apart from

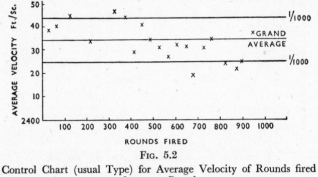

Fig. 5.2

Control Chart (usual Type) for Average Velocity of Rounds fired from one Barrel

those cases where we are directly and primarily interested in the way in which the variables influence one another.

To fix our ideas, let us think of successive batches of ammunition which are fired from one and the same barrel. The condition of the barrel will slightly alter from one batch to the next, if not from one round to the next. By how much it will change depends on the quality of the barrel steel and on the quality of the ammunition. Even if the barrel material is as it should be according to the specifications laid down for barrel steel, the changing " barrel life," that is, the ageing of the barrel with every new batch of ammunition fired from it, will influence the functioning of the ammunition, namely, its velocity and pressure. We could evade the effect of " barrel life " on these functioning characteristics of the rounds of ammunition by changing the barrel. But this would introduce a new disturbing factor due to possible differences in barrels. It is therefore advisable, if no other considerations come into play, to fire from one barrel but to take the influence of barrel life properly into account.

Let us assume that successive batches of 200 rounds each of a certain type of ammunition have been fired. If we now wish to control the quality of the ammunition with regard to its velocity, we can set up for this purpose a quality control chart of the usual kind (Fig. 5.2).

We see at once that the control chart idea in the form

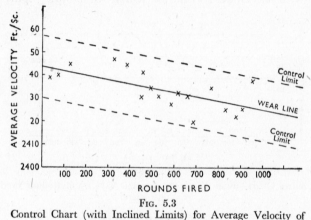

FIG. 5.3
Control Chart (with Inclined Limits) for Average Velocity of
Rounds fired from one Barrel

which is familiar to us does not fit the problem. Not taking into account barrel life, we would from the chart conclude that the quality of the ammunition as indicated by the velocity was not under control. This conclusion, however, would be wrong if the variation in the velocity which we observe were due, not so much to significant differences in quality of the ammunition, but to the influence of wear of barrel.

What is wanted, therefore, is clearly a quality control chart so designed as to take properly into account the effect of the assignable cause of barrel life. A chart on which the grand average line was not horizontal but somewhat inclined towards the horizontal would evidently meet this requirement.

On either side of that line control limits could be drawn within which all sample averages could be expected to lie if the quality of the ammunition was under control. A chart of that kind would represent a picture like the following :

The problem with which we are faced when trying to construct a chart like 5.3 is obviously this : Are there legitimate methods available for

(a) determining the *direction* of the average level ; and

(b) obtaining *control limits* which could serve a purpose analogous to that of the 1/40 and 1/1000 limits on the ordinary control chart ?

The answer is that such methods have been developed in what is called Correlation Analysis.

5.3 Correlation Between True Variables—The Correlation Table

The trend is an instance of the relation between statistical variables known as *Correlation*.

The trend, however, formed by successive sample averages if the samples are taken periodically either with regard to time or quantity of output, is not the typical case of a correlation between two variables. We have here one genuine variable—vertical scale—and one artificial—horizontal scale. The latter is only a quasi-variable, in which the series of ordinal numbers is used for the purpose of distinguishing between samples. The samples are thus ranked, not measured.

In the typical case, however, both variables are true chance variables, that is, they can take on different values with different probability. It is here that the correlation method unfolds its full power.

Let us think of a machine operation by which cartridge cases are loaded with propellant. What is essential for the functioning of the round is the amount of propellant in the cartridge case as measured by its *weight*. But the construction of the loading machine is such as to load a certain *volume*. Considering, now, that the propellant consists either of small flakes or cylinders, it is clear that one and the same weight can be more or less closely packed and could thus give slightly different volumes, and vice versa. It is evident that the correct powder charge will in such a case depend on the intensity of correlation between the volume loaded and its weight.

The diameter of the column of propellant being constant, it is, strictly speaking, the height of filling which is directly controlled by setting the machine. The weight, on the other hand, is only indirectly controlled by the intensity of correlation between the height of filling and the weight. It is therefore essential for the purpose of the whole operation to know to what extent such dependence exists. This is found in the following way :

A number of filled cases are picked at random and measured

·01″ grains \	HEIGHT										W Frequencies	H Class Mean
	100	110	120	130	140	150	160	170	180	190		
37·65												
37·45									1		1	185
37·25							1				1	165
37·05					2	3	2				7	163·6
36·85				3	3	3	3	1			13	152·0
36·65			2	9	6	6	4	3			30	155
36·45		1	4	14	7	1		1			28	137·5
36·25		1	3	5	3	1					13	135
36·05	1	2		1	2						6	127
35·85												
35·65	1										1	105
35·45												
H Frequencies	2	4	9	32	21	13	11	7	1		100	
W Class Mean	35·95	36·30	36·53	36·60	36·61	36·80	36·97	36·86	37·55			

(Left axis label: WEIGHT)

Fig. 5.4

Correlation Table

according to both characteristics—weight and height of filling. These measurements are then recorded in the form of a Correlation Table, where each individual case is entered according to its value in both variables. After having measured, say, 100 fillings, the table could present the picture Fig. 5.4 on page 110.

5.4 The Correlation Diagram

There are various methods of determining the intensity of association between two variables. We shall start with the simplest—the geometric method.

The column on the right side of the table gives the mean height for a given class interval of weight, and the bottom line the mean weight for a given class interval of height. We see at a glance that on the whole an increase in height is accompanied by an increase in weight, and vice versa. In such a case we speak of a positive correlation between the variables. If increase in one variable was accompanied by a decrease in the other, it would be a case of a negative correlation. The absence of any regularity whatsoever, or the same mean height for all the values of weight (and vice versa), would point to absence of correlation.

To represent correlation graphically we mark on the horizontal axis the class intervals for, say, height, and erect in the centre of each interval an ordinate whose length is proportional to the *mean* weight in that interval. The individual weights on which the mean is based are also entered in the following diagram (Fig. 5.5). The scale in this simplest method of graphic representation is quite arbitrary.

We find that the points so obtained can be fitted satisfactorily by a straight line, called the Regression Line. This line, which corresponds exactly to the trend on our charts, indicates the presence of correlation. If it ascends to the right it points to a positive, if to the left to a negative. A horizontal line would mean the absence of correlation.

5.5 Galton's Geometrical Method for Determining the Intensity of Correlation Between Two Variables

But this method is very primitive. As the scale for both variables is entirely arbitrary we could give our line any

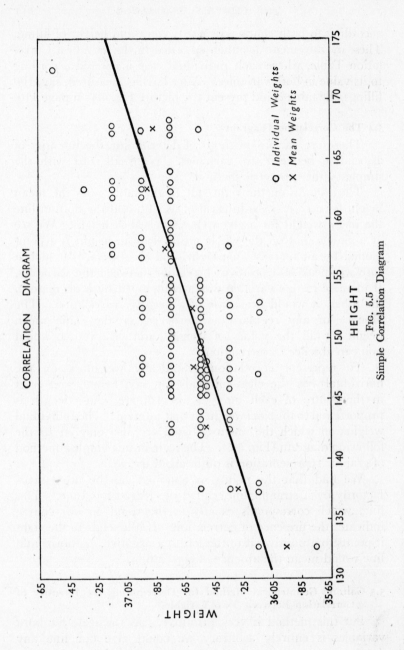

CORRELATION DIAGRAM

○ *Individual Weights*
✕ *Mean Weights*

Fig. 5.5
Simple Correlation Diagram

HEIGHT

WEIGHT

inclination we choose. We could make it steeper or flatter by appropriate changes in the scales. That is why the direction of the line cannot be safely used as a measure of the intensity of correlation. The first method as it stands cannot, therefore, be used for estimating the correlation coefficient which serves as a measure of the intensity of correlation.

If we wanted to do this geometrically we must standardize the values of the deviations in both variables. We do this by expressing them as multiples of their respective standard deviations, and therefore as pure numbers, with the result of making them comparable with one another.

Standardization means dividing by the standard deviation. We divide, say, the class interval centres of height by σ_H and get the equidistant scale on the horizontal axis. Then we divide the averages of weight in each class interval of height by σ_W and get our vertical ordinate.

The intersections of the verticals and horizontals erected at corresponding points of height and weight will again lie approximately on a straight line. But this time the inclination of the line is a reliable measure of the amount of correlation. We find the correlation coefficient as the ratio of the ordinate of a point on the regression line to its abscissa, or as the slope of the regression line (Fig. 5.6).

For our example we find that the correlation equals 0·66 approximately.

Just as we chose H as the independent variable, we could have chosen W. The vertical ordinates would then represent the centres of the standardized class intervals of W, and the horizontal ordinates the standardized *averages* of H belonging to each interval of W.

Proceeding in the same way as before, we obtain again a correlation line, but as a rule not the same line as before. What we have done at first is called " determining the regression of W on H " ; what we are doing now is to determine the regression of H on W. The lines are consequently called regression lines of W on H, or H on W, respectively.

Now it is the angle formed by these lines, or rather its *cosine*, which is a measure of the association between the two variables. This allows us in a simple way to find out all we

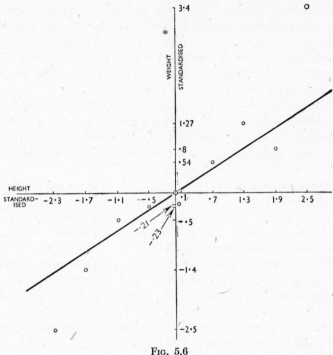

FIG. 5.6
Galton's Diagram of Correlation

want about the limiting values of the correlation co-efficient in general.

The cos of 90° is zero ; consequently, if the lines are at right angles, which means that to any value of H there corresponds always the same mean value of W, and vice versa, there is no correlation.

The cos of 0° is 1. Consequently if the lines coincide, which means that to a specified value of H there corresponds only one value of W, and vice versa, the correlation is perfect ; it has become a functional relationship.

The cos of any intermediate angle between 90° and 0° can take values between 0 and 1. Therefore the correlation co-efficient in general can take values between 0 and 1, and in the case of negative correlation between 0 and —1.

As both regression lines must necessarily lie in the same

quadrant, we can easily see what position will indicate the maximum positive correlation, namely 1. Let us assume the angle between the two regression lines, whose position with regard to their respective independent axis is always similar, is anything between 0° and 90°. Now let us move both lines towards one another until they coincide, keeping their position with regard to their respective axes similar. They will then coincide when the angle of inclination of each line towards its axis is 45°. This position of a regression line halving the quadrant then indicates the maximum of correlation.

The corresponding line for perfect negative correlation is inclined under 135° towards the axis of the independent variable. Any positive correlation less than 1 must be represented by a regression line whose angle of inclination towards the axis of the independent variable is less than 45°.

5.6 The Correlation Coefficient Computed by the Product–Moment Formula—The Regression Equation

But any graphic method has its mathematical shortcomings. If it is a question of obtaining a correct measure of the intensity of correlation between two variables, an arithmetical method is recommended.

The algebraic formula for the correlation coefficient is the Product-Moment formula, or Bravais formula :

$$r = \frac{S f D_x D_y}{N \sigma_x \sigma_y} \quad . \qquad . \qquad . \qquad . \qquad . \qquad (5.1a)$$

where f = Frequencies

D = Deviation from resp. Means

S = operation of Summing

which in the case of the deviations being taken from an arbitrary mean becomes

$$r = \frac{S a_x a_y - N b_x b_y}{N \sigma_x \sigma_y} \quad . \qquad . \qquad . \qquad . \qquad (5.1b)$$

where a_x, a_y = deviations from resp. arbitrary values A_x, A_y. (For meaning of b see Appendix II)

As an illustration let us use the data of Table 5.4. The following diagram (5.7) and paragraphs exhibit the procedure for employing the Product Moment formula step by step.

(Step 1) It is very advantageous to express both the deviations from A and the standard deviations as multiples of the class intervals, because this reduces the amount of computation considerably.

Care must be taken that all quantities in the formula for r are expressed in the same units ; either all as actual deviations from A_x, A_y, or all as multiples of class intervals.

We now divide the table by the cross through A_x and A_y into four quadrants, and mark the deviations as multiples of

	0·01 in. grains	-4 100	-3 110	-2 120	-1 130	0 140 ($A_H=145$)	1 150	2 160	3 170	4 180	190	f_W	$fa_Ha_W +$	$fa_Ha_W -$
5	37.45									1_{20}		1	20	
4	37.25							1_{8}				1	8	
3	37.05						2_{3}	3_{6}	2_{9}			7	6,18,18	
2	36.85				3_{-2}	3_{0}	3_{2}	3_{4}	1_{6}			13	6,12,6	6
1	36.65			2_{-2}	9_{-1}	6_{0}	6_{1}	4_{2}	3_{3}			30	6,8,9	4,9
$A_W=36.55$ 0	36.45		1_{0}	4_{0}	14_{0}	7_{0}	1_{0}		1_{0}			28		
-1	36.25		1_{3}	3_{2}	5_{1}	3_{0}	1_{-1}					13	3,6,5	1
-2	36.05	1_{8}	2_{6}		1_{2}	2_{0}						6	8,12,2	
-3	35.85													
-4	35.65	1_{16}										1	16	
-5	35.45													
f_H		2	4	9	32	21	13	11	7	1		100	168	20

$$S f a_H a_W = 148$$

FIG. 5.7

Correlation Table adjusted for Calculating the Correlation Coefficient

NOTES

(1) The outer scales represent the deviations from the arbitrary Means, $A_W A_H$, in multiples of the Class Intervals.

(2) The figure in the lower right-hand corner of a square represents the product of the deviations a_W and a_H, from A_W and A_H respectively.

(3) The last columns contain the positive and negative products $fa_H a_W$ whose algebraic sum gives the term $S f a_H a_W$.

class intervals. A product of the form $fa_x a_y$ is then clearly the product of the deviations of a given square from both A_x and A_y times the frequency (f) entered in the square.

(Step 2) In this way the algebraic sum of all these products is formed, and care should be taken to give each product the proper sign ; the right-hand upper quadrant and the left-hand lower quadrant being positive, the other two negative. The products within the cross are, of course, all zero, the A_x, A_y being zero. We thus obtain 148 for $Sfa_x a_y$.

We now turn to the quantity in the denominator of $(5.1b)$ (see Appendix I for calculation of M,σ).

(Step 3) *Height.*

$$M_H = A_H + (b_H \times 10\,*) = 145 + \left\{ \left[\frac{\text{S(Deviations from } A_H)}{100} \right] \times 10 \right\}$$

$$= 145 + \{ -\cdot 1 \times 10 \} = 145 - 1 = 144 \quad \begin{array}{l} \text{(Units :} \\ \cdot 01 \text{ of an} \\ \text{inch)} \end{array}$$

Standard Deviation $\sigma_H = \left(\sqrt{\dfrac{\text{S(Deviations from } A_H)^2}{100} - b_H{}^2} \right) \times 10$

$$= \{ \sqrt{2\cdot72 - \cdot01} \} \times 10 = 1\cdot65 \times 10 = 16\cdot5 \text{ (in } \cdot01\text{'s of an inch)}$$

(Step 4) *Weight.*

$$M_W = A_W + (b_W \times \cdot2\,*) = 36\cdot55 + \left\{ \left[\frac{\text{S(Deviations from } A_W)}{100} \right] \times \cdot2 \right\}$$

$$= 36\cdot55 + (\cdot55 \times \cdot2) = 36\cdot55 + \cdot11 = 36\cdot66 \text{ grains}$$

Standard Deviation $\sigma_W = \left\{ \sqrt{\dfrac{\text{S(Deviations from } A_W)^2}{100} - b_W{}^2} \right\} \times \cdot2$

$$= \{ \sqrt{2\cdot31 - \cdot30} \} \times \cdot2 = 1\cdot41 \times \cdot2 = \cdot28 \text{ grains}$$

(Step 5) Combining the results of steps 2, 3, 4 we have

$$r_{HW} = \frac{\text{S(Deviations from } M_H \times \text{Deviations from } M_W)}{100 \sigma_H \sigma_H}$$

$$= \frac{\text{S(Dev. from } A_H \times \text{Dev. from } A_W) - 100\, b_H b_W}{100 \sigma_H / 10 \times \sigma_W / \cdot2} \quad \begin{array}{l} \text{(see formula 5.1}b\text{ and} \\ \text{step 1)} \end{array}$$

$$= \frac{148 - (100 \times -\cdot1 \times \cdot55)}{100 \times 1\cdot65 \times 1\cdot41} = \frac{153\cdot5}{232\cdot65} = \underline{\underline{\cdot66}}$$

* Class interval size

Knowing how to calculate the correlation coefficient, we are now in a position to substitute for the somewhat crude method of drawing the best-fitting line to our scatter of points simply free-hand a more ambitious one. We can calculate its position and, knowing the correlation coefficient, the way for doing this has been made very smooth indeed.

If r is the correlation coefficient between height and weight, and we want the regression line of W on H, all we have to do is this :

We form the quantity $r\dfrac{\sigma_W}{\sigma_H}$ and write the equations for the regression line of W on H as

$$(\overline{W} - M_w) = r\frac{\sigma_W}{\sigma_H} (H - M_H), \quad . \quad . \quad . \quad (5.2)$$

where r is the correlation coefficient, σ_W, σ_H have their usual meaning as standard deviations of W and H, M_w and M_H stand for the respective mean values, and where $\overline{W}$ stands for the mean value of the W-array belonging to a given H.

By substituting successive values of H (class interval centres) we obtain corresponding values of $\overline{W}$ and can plot the regression line as the line through such co-ordinated pairs of values of H and W (Fig. 5.8).

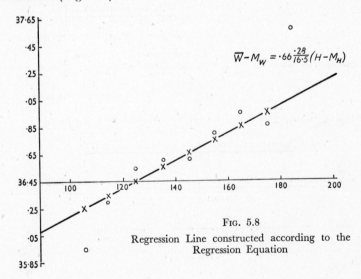

$$\overline{W} - M_W = \cdot 66\frac{\cdot 28}{16\cdot 5}(H - M_H)$$

Fig. 5.8

Regression Line constructed according to the Regression Equation

A similar equation, and regression line, may be obtained giving $\bar{H}$ in terms of W (Regression of H on W):

$$(\bar{H} - M_H) = r\frac{\sigma_H}{\sigma_W} (W - M_W) \quad \text{(see Fig. 5.5}a\text{)}.$$

This provides the answer to Part I of the problem stated at the end of paragraph 5.2.

5.7 The Part of the Variance of the Dependent Variable which Remains Unexplained by Correlation

We now understand enough of the mechanism of correlation to tackle the problem of how to make use of it for the purpose of obtaining control limits. (Part II of the problem stated at the end of paragraph 5.4.)

It can easily be shown that if the measure of correlation between two variables is R, then the part of the total variance of the variable Y, say, that is accounted for, or explained by, the variation of the other variable, X, is the square of the standard deviation of Y, σ_y^2 multiplied by R^2. In other words, it is the fraction of σ_y^2 given by $\sigma_y^2 R^2$. R^2 must always be a fraction unless R = zero (no correlation) or R = 1 (functional relationship).

The total variance of Y, σ_y^2, will thus consist of two parts

$$\sigma_y^2 = \sigma_y^2 R^2 + \text{Remainder} \quad . \quad . \quad . \quad (5.2)$$

The " Remainder " term is the part of the variance of Y which is left unexplained by Y's relation to X. There are now two principal measures of correlation, which we call the Correlation Ratio (η) and the Correlation Co-efficient (r). According to which of these we substitute for the R in formula (5.2), the " remainder " term will take on a different meaning.

5.8 The Remainder Term in the Case of the Correlation Ratio (η)

Let us first look at Fig. 5.5. The points in a given column represent the values of Y (Weight) belonging to a given value of X (Height). It is evident that the smaller the range of the Y's *within* these columns, the surer can a change in X be taken to import a change in Y. The more wider spaced they are, that is, the greater the range within a column, the more will they overlap from one column to the next or even the next but one, etc., and the less reliably does a change in X carry with it a corresponding change in Y. Each column has its own frequency distribution, and the degree of variability within these partial distributions determines the intensity of correlation between the variables.

Now the most reliable measure for the range of variation is the standard deviation. If we calculate that parameter of dispersion for each of the columns, then the average of all the squares of these partial standard deviations will give a dependable measure of the extent to which a change in X is accompanied by a change in Y, or to what extent Y is controlled by X. The *greater* the average square of the standard deviation the *less* can we rely upon a change in X producing a corresponding change in Y, and vice versa.

According to this interpretation, the average square of the partial standard deviations, or to be exact, the average of the squared deviations of all observations from their respective Array Means, should be equal to what we have called above the " remainder " term in equation (5.2). And this is actually the case. It is the part of the variance of Y which is left unaccounted for by its correlation with X. Calling the (partial) deviations of the Y's within a column from their respective sub-means, Z, we have, forming one total distribution of all Z's,

$$\sigma_y{}^2 = \sigma_y{}^2 \, R^2 + \sigma_z{}^2 \quad \cdots \cdots \quad (5.3a)$$

and
$$\sigma_z{}^2 = \sigma_y{}^2 \, (1 - R^2). \quad \cdots \cdots \quad (5.3b)$$

The ratio
$$\frac{\sigma_z}{\sigma_y} = \sqrt{1 - R^2}. \quad \cdots \cdots \quad (5.3c)$$

is a measure of the extent to which Y is *not* dependent on X and is called the Coefficient of Alienation.

The quantity
$$R = \sqrt{1 - \frac{\sigma_z{}^2}{\sigma_y{}^2}} \quad \cdots \cdots \quad (5.3d)$$

is called the Correlation Ratio, and is usually denoted by η. It measures the intensity of correlation between X and Y, no matter what the form of the relationship.

From the above formulae we see that for $\sigma_z = 0, \therefore \eta = 1$, and for $\sigma_z = \sigma_y, \therefore \eta = 0$.

In words : If the standard deviation within the columns is zero, η must be 1 because to a given value of X there corresponds then only one value of Y. If σ_z equals the standard deviation of Y, η must be zero, because for a given value of X there would be the whole range of Y's to choose from.

5.9 Translation Into the Control Chart Picture

Let us now translate all this into the familiar form of the control chart.

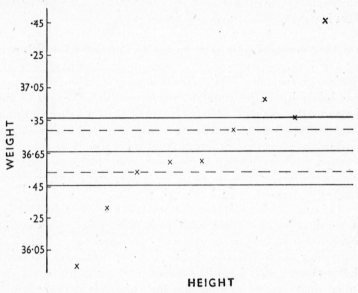

FIG. 5.9
Control Chart for Weight using Sub-groups of Height

On the horizontal scale are marked the class intervals of the variable height, on the vertical scale those of the variable weight. We then plot the averages of W from each column of Table 5.5 against the proper class interval value of H. The control limits are obtained from the average range or standard deviation within the columns.

We see that the averages show a definite trend upwards, indicating a shifting mean. The correlation ratio can be taken as a measure of the extent to which a trend might be expected, and therefore indicates to what extent we must expect our product to be out of statistical control. In our case it indicates to what extent weight is not under statistical control if we sub-group according to class intervals of height. (This does not mean, however, that it must appear out of control if the sub-grouping was done according to other variables, " time," for instance ; see paragraph 5.1.)

This means that the usual type of control chart can in such cases only give an indication of the lack of control, but cannot effectively be used for controlling the characteristic as the term is used in quality control work.

5.10 The Remainder Term in the Case of the Correlation Coefficient (r)

The interpretation of the " remainder " term of formula (5.3) as given above, and that of the measure of correlation, η, was based upon the standard deviation of the arrays of the dependent variable. There is, however, another possible conception of the " remainder " which yields a measure of correlation somewhat different from the correlation ratio. It is called the Correlation Coefficient, r, and is the measure most commonly used. This measure can best be explained from the regression diagram, Fig. 5.5.

Looking at that diagram, we see that the individual values of Y belonging to a given value of X do not lie exactly on the regression line, but are more or less scattered around it. The closer they are to the line, the surer could predictions be made that a change in X would be followed by a change in Y ; the wider their scatter around the line, the less reliably will a change in X purport a change in Y.

Thus the intensity of correlation will in this case depend upon the scatter of the Y's, not exactly around their own sub-means as before, but around the regression line. Using the standard deviation of the deviations of these points—measured along the Y axis—from the regression line as the best measure of dispersion, we arrive at an interpretation of the " remainder " as the variance (square of standard deviation) of the deviations of the Y's from the regression line, measured on the Y axis. Calling these deviations residuals, Z', we now define the remainder as the variance of the residuals Z'. As the quantities Z' will as a rule be more or less different from the quantities Z, and, therefore, $\sigma_{z'}$ different from σ_z, we must expect the fraction R^2 in equations (5.3) to have here a somewhat different meaning from η^2. This is actually the case. The quantity which now takes the place of η is the Coefficient of Correlation, r, which we have already met in paragraph 5.6, where the working formula for it was given. It is a measure of the *linear* dependence between two variables.

The form of equations 5.3a to 5.3d remains unchanged. Thus

$$\sigma_y{}^2 = \sigma_y{}^2 r^2 + \sigma_{z'}{}^2 \quad \cdot \quad \cdot \quad \cdot \quad \cdot \quad \cdot \quad \cdot \quad (5.4a)$$

$$\sigma_z{}^2 = \sigma_y{}^2 (1 - r^2) \quad \cdot \quad \cdot \quad \cdot \quad \cdot \quad \cdot \quad \cdot \quad (5.4b)$$

$$\frac{\sigma_{z'}{}^2}{\sigma_y{}^2} = 1 - r^2 \quad \cdot \quad \cdot \quad \cdot \quad \cdot \quad \cdot \quad \cdot \quad (5.4c)$$

$$r^2 = \sqrt{1 - \frac{\sigma_{z'}{}^2}{\sigma_y{}^2}} \quad \cdot \quad \cdot \quad \cdot \quad \cdot \quad \cdot \quad \cdot \quad (5.4d)$$

5.11 A Test for Linearity of Regression

The comparison of η with r for one and the same bi-variate universe allows us to draw a conclusion as to whether the correlation is linear. Multiplying both numerator and denominator of $\frac{\sigma_z{}^2}{\sigma_y{}^2}$ by N, the number of observations, which leaves it unchanged, we can express the relation (5.3c) in words thus :

$$1 - \eta^2{}_{yx} = \frac{\text{Sum of Squares of Deviations from } Array \text{ Means of Y}}{\text{Sum of Squared Deviations from } General \text{ Mean of Y}} \quad (5.5b)$$

or

$$1 - \eta^2{}_{xy} = \frac{\text{Sum of Squares of Deviations from } Array \text{ Means of X}}{\text{Sum of Squared Deviations from } General \text{ Mean of X}} \quad (5.5a)$$

For formula (5.4c) we have :

$$1 - r_{xy}{}^2 = \frac{\text{Sum of Squares of Deviations from Linear Regression Line}}{\text{Total Sum of Squared Deviations from either } \bar{x} \text{ or } \bar{y}} \quad (5.6)$$

Considering now that the sum of squared deviations from the mean is a minimum, that is, smaller than from any other value,* it follows that $1 - r^2$ cannot be less than $1 - \eta^2$. Furthermore, that the more the line connecting the array means deviates from the straight line (regression line), the

* see Appendix II

more pronounced will become the difference between $1 - r^2$ and $1 - \eta^2$, the former getting greater and greater.

Consequently r^2 must become increasingly smaller than η^2 with increased curvilinearity of correlation. This is used as a test for linearity, or otherwise, of correlation.

5.12 The Standard Error of Estimate—Control by Correlation

$\sigma_{z'} = \sigma_y \sqrt{1 - r^2}$ is called the Standard Error of Estimate, and has a function similar to that of the Standard Error of an Average. (The difference between the estimated Y and its true value is, in fact, the error of an average, because in the equation for the regression of Y on X, Y stands for the average of Y's belonging to a given X.) It is a measure of the confidence that can be placed in the prediction that a particular X will produce the average value of Y given by the ordinate of the regression line corresponding to that particular X.

The Y's of a particular array belonging to a given X will differ more or less from their " true " value—taking the estimated Y on the regression line to be that " true " value—according to the intensity of correlation. The standard error of estimate now indicates the range on both sides of a particular Y within which to expect with a certain probability the " true " value to lie, and, conversely, the range on both sides of the regression line within which for a given X to expect with a certain probability the observed Y's to lie.

This suggests—assuming a normal distribution of the residuals—the use of control lines by taking three times $\sigma_{z'}$ on either side of the regression line as the limits within which all Y's can be expected to lie, and two times $\sigma_{z'}$, as including 95 per cent. of the plotted points (Fig. 5.10).

For the purpose of control, the standard error of estimate is determined for the pair of variables as it results from the best possible performance of both, machine and operator, using standard material. From that standard error, control limits are obtained in the usual way. Should subsequent inspection, carried out at specified intervals, yield points falling outside the control limits at two respectively three times the standard error in greater than the assigned proportions, this is taken as in indication that the intensity of dependence

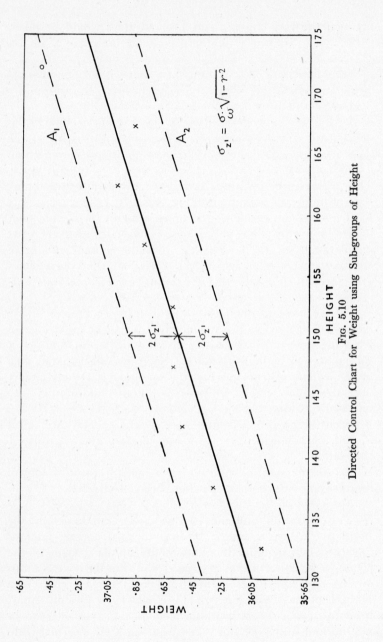

$$\sigma_{z_1} = \sigma_\omega \cdot \sqrt{1 - r^2}$$

HEIGHT

Fig. 5.10

Directed Control Chart for Weight using Sub-groups of Height

125

between the variables was relaxed, and steps would be taken with a view to ascertaining and removing the cause of such a disturbance.

Such limits are control limits in a somewhat different sense of the term from that which we have encountered hitherto.

First, on the practical side :

What we are concerned with here is not so much the question of whether one *particular* column shows a Y greater than it ought to (although even that question can become important), but to what extent Y *in general* is controlled by X. This information is provided by the distance between our control lines measured along the Y axis.

The direction of the regression line itself can provide such information only if the variables are standardized ; then, its inclination between 0 and 45° will indicate the amount of correlation varying between 0 and 1. But the control lines at ± three times $\sigma_{y'}$ will do that also and even *without* standardization.

All we have to do is to read the distance between these lines on the Y scale and it will give us a very good idea of what the state of control is like, getting all information about this matter in a single distance. Such visual or spatial idea of the extent of association will sometimes have advantages over the usual method of compressing the information into one single parameter, because it shows the amount of overlap between the partial distributions of the dependent variable at a glance, upon which, as we know, depends the intensity of correlation.

Thus, direction of regression lines and distance of control limits supplement one another here very effectively.

Secondly, on the theoretical side :

The control limits on the chart for *averages* are three times the standard error of the *averages*, those on the chart for the standard deviation or range are three times the standard error of the standard deviation or ranges respectively. But the control limits on the *correlation* diagram must not be taken to represent a multiple of the standard error of the *correlation* coefficient. Apart from our scanty theoretical knowledge of that type of error for non-normal universes, this is not what we are concerned with.

If we were interested in the variations of the direction of the regression line representing different samples from one and the same universe, then we would have to take the standard error of the correlation coefficient into account.*

Although this question of the significance of the correlation coefficient obtained from a sample may become very important, especially if the sample was small, we can fortunately evade that complication by working with large samples of, say, 100 to 300. For our purpose it is more important to obtain a really good working idea of what a certain *amount of* R *means*, and this we can get by the method described above. The distance between the $\pm 3\sigma_{z'}$ lines, read off the Y scale, shows at a glance the variability of the Y's belonging to a given X. Further, we see immediately the amount of overlap between neighbouring columns, and can thus get a very good idea to what extent a change in X controls a change in Y. We also see the steps by which Y increases per unit increase in X.

5.13 The Compass of Chance

Let us still further realize how our idea of control lines has changed if we speak of the lines A_1, A_2 in Fig. 5.10 as control lines.

They are what might be called " directed control lines." By this is meant that it is not only their *position* which matters now but also their *direction*. We can, under certain conditions, read the amount of correlation between the variables, represented on our two scales, from their inclination toward the horizontal. Generally, their direction is no longer one and the same on all charts, as is the case with our former control limits, but depends on the amount of correlation between the variables. That is why the simile of the *Compass* has been chosen for the heading of this chapter.

Let us suppose that a ship to whose captain definite sailing orders have been given at the commencement of the journey had arrived at her destination, and we were asked to find from the log book whether the ship's course had always been in conformity with those orders. The course according to the

---

* For a brief and clear account of the sampling error of r, see Levy and Preidel, *Elementary Statistics*, Nelson's Aeroscience Manuals, 1944

sailing directions we call the " intended course." It can be thought of as a specified direction. Studying now the log book day by day, we can ascertain to what extent that direction was adhered to. We shall find, no doubt, that, on the whole, the ship was steered in compliance with her intended course, but wind and weather might not always have permitted her to do so completely. There is also the possibility of deviation from the intended course because of inefficiency on the part of the officer or men in charge, and because of inherent short-comings in the construction of the ship and her machinery.

The degree to which the sailing direction was actually adhered to could be represented graphically by plotting the actual position of the ship, day by day, or watch by watch. We should then find that these points are arrayed around the line (straight line or smooth curve) representing the intended course. The sum of the squared daily deviations from that line divided by the total number of observations (giving the square of the standard deviation of the actual positions from the intended course) will give a good idea of the extent to which the officer in command had been able to make the ship carry out her sailing orders. The better he was able to do this, the smaller would be the standard deviation. If we drew " control limits " at two or three times that standard deviation, then the distance between such limits would be a good indication of the extent to which the ship's course has been " under control."

In the same way we can think of our control limits around the regression line as indicating, by the distance between them, to what extent one variable (the dependent one) was controlled by the other, a small distance indicating a high degree, a wide a low degree, of control.

But as *omne simile claudicat*, our analogy should not be pressed too far. In Figs. 5.5, 5.10 we cannot regard the *direction* of the regression line, and therefore of the control limits, as a reliable indication of anything ; only the *distance* between the control limits would be indicative of the amount of correlation. In Fig. 5.6, on the other hand, we have in the direction of the regression line already a measure of the amount of association between our variables, and the distance between the control limits is, therefore, here dependent on their direction. As the angle of inclination increases from 0° to 45°, that distance becomes smaller and smaller. The "intended course" of a ship, however, gives by itself the direction, and the deviations of the actual course from that theoretical course do not stand in a functional relationship to its direction.

But in spite of such shortcomings in our analogy, I believe that it will serve to bring out the essential difference between control charts with horizontal and inclined control limits, and so contribute towards making a difficult distinction clearer.

5.14 Summary

A. The disadvantage of the simple graph method for showing correlations is that the inclination of the regression line is no measure of correlation.

The disadvantage of the Galton method is the complexity of procedure. Now the use of control limits in the sense described above makes it possible to retain the simple method, and yet obtain a very good idea of the intensity of correlation.

It is, of course, possible to provide the Galton diagram with control limits, and so supplement the summary information obtained from that diagram as to the amount of correlation by the more detailed one of the standard error of estimate.

B. The study of simple correlation has thus led to an important generalization of the control line idea.*

The horizontal control lines appear to be a special kind of control lines, only applicable if there was no correlation between the characteristic in question and the characteristic used for sub-grouping (*control by chance causes*).

If, however, such correlation exists, and randomness is disturbed, we can still use control lines which are so designed as to provide the information we are after in such cases. What we want to know in such cases is to what extent our primarily important characteristic is effectively controlled by another characteristic which is directly accessible to measurement (*control by assignable causes*).

In the example given we have, for instance, found that approximately 44 per cent. of the variance of weight was con-

* For a case of elliptical control lines, see G. Herdan, "The Analysis of Colour," *British Science News*, 1947, vol. i, 4

trolled by height of filling ($r^2 = \cdot66^2 = \cdot4356$), and if we are satisfied that for the performance in question such control is sufficient, that measure of dependence should form part of the specifications for filling by height.

Considerations of that kind must, whether they are explicitly aware of it or not, form the basis for the management's decision to use a machine by which a certain characteristic can only be indirectly controlled.

5.15 Illustration for Curvilinear Regression

(*a*) For the proper functioning of cartridge cases it is required that, at specified intervals along the case, the hardness of the metal be of a certain degree. This can also be expressed by saying that the gradient of hardness at specified points along the case should not exceed certain limits.

We thus arrive, as a fundamental requirement for good functioning of the case, at a correlation between distance measured along the case and hardness of metal. The regression curve is a rather complicated one, as shown in the following diagram :

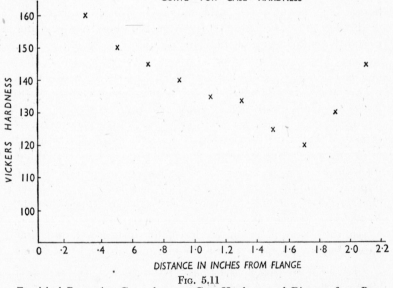

FIG. 5.11

Empirical Regression Curve between Case Hardness and Distance from Base

(b) The assignable causes for hardness are mainly these :

   (i) The quality of the metal strip from which the discs are obtained, which are transformed into the cases ;

   (ii) the operation of the machine which draws the metal discs out into the case ; and

   (iii) the semi-annealing and tip annealing operations.

It is evident that these main assignable causes must be controlled, in the engineering sense of the term, in order that the cases should have the required gradient of hardness. A continuous check on production, with a view to finding out whether or not the product complies with the requirements regarding hardness, can be achieved by means of a quality control chart of a peculiar kind. In this type of chart use is made of the correlation between the distance along the case and the hardness of the metal. It is evident that the distance of the case does not " control " the hardness in the engineering sense of the term. Such control can only be achieved by controlling the assignable causes. But we can make use of the correlation between distance along the case and hardness for satisfying ourselves during mass production that these assignable causes are working in just the way in which they should work. That is, that they are blended so as to produce cases according to specifications.

(c) In order to construct a quality control chart of that kind we must first obtain the correlation curve between distance and hardness. As the curve is rather a complicated one, we obtain it graphically. We select a number of cases, say 100, of which we know that the hardness more or less satisfies specifications, take the mean hardness at each of the specified points, connect those means by a continuous curve, and so obtain the regression curve graphically.

What we are now interested in is to know the control limits which will enable us to separate chance deviations from deviations brought about by significant changes in the assignable causes. For this purpose we must know the standard error of estimate for our regression curve. To obtain this we proceed in the following way.

A point on the curve at a specified distance along the case length is obtained as an average of a distribution of points (array of points). We now form the sum of squares of deviations of the points (constituting such an array) from the array mean, sum for all arrays, divide by the sum of squares of deviations of *all* hardness measurements from the general mean, and subtract the result from unity. This gives us the square of the correlation ratio, η^2. The standard error of estimate can now be obtained as the product of the standard deviation of the total of hardness measurements by $\sqrt{1 - \eta^2}$ (equation 5.3c).

The inner control limits will be at a distance of twice and the outer control limits at a distance of three times the standard error of estimate on either side of the regression curve. As seen from the following diagram (Fig. 5.12), this gives us a band within which hardness measurements at specified intervals are allowed to vary without justifying the suspicion that an undesirable change in one of the assignable causes has occurred. A hardness measurement outside that band, however, would indicate such a change, and, consequently, point to the necessity of investigating the matter.

(d) In order to use the above method for continuous checking of mass production some modification must be made in the charting. First of all, we are only interested in the case-hardness at specified points. We therefore need not have a continuous curve. Secondly, we want a chart drawn up in such a way as to enable us to plot at specified intervals a great number of examination results—that is, of successive samples of cases.

As can be seen from the following diagram, the fact that we are only interested in the case-hardness at specified discrete points along the case length enables us to meet the second requirement.

Instead of putting a continuous curve on the chart, we put disconnected horizontal lines at the regression level of hardness for the specified points along the case length, and parallel to these also disconnected horizontal lines at twice and three times the standard error of estimate. We then plot the inspection results for each specified distance from the lower end of the case, one beside the other, a case being represented by a dot at each hardness level. According to the length of the horizontal lines we have chosen—and that again depends on the dimensions

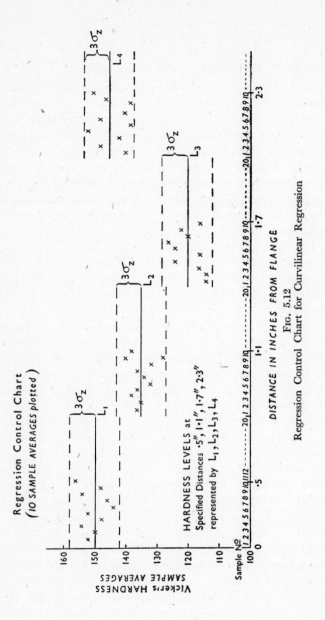

Fig. 5.12
Regression Control Chart for Curvilinear Regression

of our chart—we then can use the chart for recording the results of a great number of successive samples.

5.16 Multiple Correlation

So far we have been concerned in this chapter with the mutual dependence of two characteristics. Although it is not the purpose of this first introduction to correlation methods to discuss in detail the intricacies of partial and multiple correlations which arise in the investigation of an effect conceived as depending upon the combined action of a number of " independent " variable causes, a brief outline of how to proceed in such cases will be given in this paragraph, since in industrial research work we are very often confronted with problems of this type.

The multiple correlation analysis can be performed by means of formulae for partial correlation coefficients—for the net effect of one independent cause upon the dependent variable—a procedure which can be recommended only if such formulae are fully understood. It is, however, possible, just as in the case of multi-variate analysis of variance, to simplify the analysis, sacrificing elegance of mathematical procedure to real understanding, by taking out the effect of one variable at a time. This procedure is here called the technique of " *successive elimination*," of which this paragraph gives a brief outline.*

The experimental data on which I propose to demonstrate the method were obtained from an experiment on corrosion of steel, whose object was to ascertain the dependence of the corrosion effect upon (1) time of exposure, and (2) thickness of a protective film. Thirty steel panels were exposed to weathering conditions, and the loss of weight due to corrosion was recorded for each panel whose film thickness was also ascertained at certain time intervals. In Fig. 5.13, the loss of weight due to corrosion is plotted against time of exposure for these thirty panels. Assuming a linear regression between the two quantities—which is, however, only approximately true—we obtain the correlation coefficient by any of the methods

---

* For a full account of this very important technique the reader is referred to M. Ezekiel, *Methods of Correlation Analysis*, J. Wiley & Sons, New York, 1941

explained in this chapter, which enables us to construct the regression line according to paragraph 5.6.

There is, however, no need for calculating the coefficient of correlation if what we are interested in is primarily the form, and not so much the amount, of dependence between our variables. In such a case, we can calculate the two constants of the linear regression line directly. Calling the loss of weight due to corrosion Y, and the time of exposure X, we have for the slope of the regression line,

$$b_{yx} = \frac{\Sigma XY - nM_xM_y}{\Sigma X^2 - nM_x^2} * \quad . \quad . \quad . \quad . \quad . \quad . \quad (5.8)$$

In order to understand how this formula is connected with those used previously in para. 5.6 for the correlation coefficient, r, and for the coefficient of regression $\left(\frac{r\sigma_w}{\sigma_H}\right)$, let us write for the

latter $\quad b_{yx} = r\,\frac{\sigma_y}{\sigma_x}\,; \quad b_{xy} = r\,\frac{\sigma_x}{\sigma_y},$

and since $\quad r = \dfrac{\Sigma xy}{n\sigma_x\sigma_y}$ . . . . (5.1a)

$$b_{yx} = \frac{\Sigma xy}{n\sigma_x\sigma_y} \cdot \frac{\sigma_y}{\sigma_x} = \frac{\Sigma xy}{n\sigma_x^2}\,; \quad b_{xy} = \frac{\Sigma xy}{n\sigma_y^2} \quad . \quad . \quad . \quad . \quad (5.8a)$$

Using instead of x and y which are the deviations from the respective means, the original measurements X and Y, equations (5.8a) become

$$b_{yx} = \frac{\Sigma XY - nM_xM_y}{\Sigma X^2 - nM_x^2}\,; \quad b_{xy} = \frac{\Sigma XY - nM_xM_y}{\Sigma Y^2 - nM_x^2}$$

For the intercept on the Y-axis we have

$$a = M_y - b_{yx}.\,M_x \quad . \quad . \quad . \quad . \quad . \quad (5.9)$$

which relation is obtained simply by substituting in the general form of the linear regression equation $y = a + bx$ for x and y the corresponding means and for the constant b the slope b_{yx}.

Calculated in this way, the regression line showing the dependence of corrosion upon time results as

$$Y' = 0{\cdot}058 + 0{\cdot}025\,X \quad . \quad . \quad . \quad . \quad . \quad . \quad (5.10)$$

* Σ standing for " the sum of all . . ."

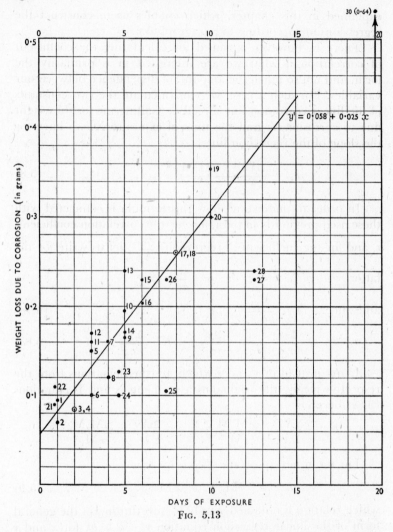

Fig. 5.13

This means that one day exposure to the weathering tests produces, on the whole, a weight loss due to corrosion of 0·025 g.

But this is clearly not the whole story. We have here implicitly assumed—apart from the linearity of the relation—that time was the only factor responsible for the severity of the corrosion effect. There is, however, as we know, another factor which might conceivably influence the corrosion effect, viz. the thickness of the protective film. We must, therefore, correct the picture for the film effect.

The first thing to do is to take the time effect out of the total corrosion effect, or, as we say, to " adjust " the weight loss for the time effect. Such " adjusting " is done either by calculating the weight loss with time according to equation (5.10), and subtracting the quantities so obtained from the observed weight loss of the panel in question, or, graphically, by measuring along the Y-axis, the distance of the plotted points from the regression line (Fig. 5.13). In this way, the weight loss due to time is taken out of the total weight loss, and these numerical differences or distances representing the variation in weight loss due to variation in film thickness (or, may be due to other factors as well) are now plotted against the individual film thickness of the thirty panels (Fig. 5.14).

Comparing the resulting scatter with that of the original observations, we notice at a glance how much in the latter was due to the time factor. We now calculate the regression line exactly as before, and obtain the equation

$$Y'' = 0.164 - 0.575 \, Z \quad . \quad . \quad . \quad . \quad . \quad . \quad . \quad (5.11)$$

Since Y'' represents the weight loss adjusted for the time effect, equation 5.11 must necessarily give the *net* effect of film thickness on corrosion, viz. that a unit increase in film thickness means a reduction of weight loss by 0.575 g.

We cannot combine both regression equations, since equation 5.10 does not yet represent the net effect of time on corrosion. We now repeat for the time factor what we have done for the film thickness factor. That is, we adjust the total weight loss for the net effect of film thickness, either numerically by subtracting each Y'' obtained by equation 5.11 from the corresponding observed Y, or graphically from Fig. 5.14, and plot the residuals against time. This means that we have now plotted the net effect of time on corrosion against time. The regression equation results as

$$Y'' = 0.047 + 0.026 \, X$$

which differs only slightly from equation 5.10.

Combining now the equations for the net effects, or for the

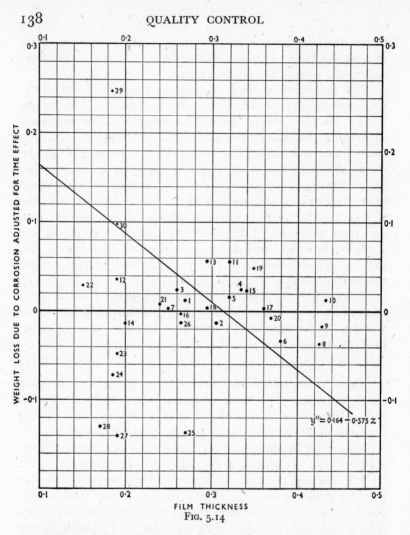

FIG. 5.14

partial regression, of our two independent variables we cbtain the multiple regression equation

$$Y'' = 0 \cdot 211 + 0 \cdot 026 \, X - 0 \cdot 575 \, Z \quad . \quad . \quad . \quad . \quad . \quad (5.12)$$

which tells us how the corrosion effect is influenced by time of exposure and film thickness, viz. that one day exposure will, on the whole, result in a weight loss of $0 \cdot 026$ g., and that one unit increases in film thickness will, on the whole, mean a decrease in weight loss of $0 \cdot 575$ g.

CHAPTER VI

"DEFECTIVES" AS ACCIDENTS—QUALITATIVE CONTROL CHARTS

6.1 Distribution of Repeated Events — The Statistical Theory of Accidents

WE are by now used to the idea of chance deviations of measurements obeying a certain kind of law, which we call the Normal Law. But it might be very surprising to hear that the type of chance events which we call *accidents* also obeys a law. Let us realize what is meant by this.

It was in the second half of the nineteenth century that a Russian statistician, Bortkiewicz, hit upon the following idea. In order to find out whether there was any regularity in a great number of evidently unconnected accidental occurrences of one and the same type, he investigated a seemingly erratic event—death by kick of a horse in the Prussian Army. He collected information about ten Prussian Army Corps over a period of twenty years, and then grouped the observations according to whether 0, 1, 2, 3, and so forth, accidents of this kind had occurred per year per Army Corps. This yielded the following frequency distribution (second column) : *

DEATHS	FREQUENCY	
Per year per army corps	Observed	Expected
0	109	108·67
1	65	66·29
2	22	20·22
3	3	4·11
4	1	·63
5	—	·08
6	—	·01

If we were to plot this frequency distribution on graph paper we would get a very different shape from the normal

* L. Bortkiewicz, *Law of Small Numbers*, Leipzig 1897

curve. It would give a J-shaped distribution, or rather a reversed J-shape if we took the origin, as is customary, on the left side. The graph would be highest at zero, and would approach the horizontal axis more and more the greater the frequency of accidents in the chosen interval.

It then occurred to Bortkiewicz that a certain mathematical formula, which was arrived at many years ago by a French mathematician, Poisson, for the distribution of statistically rare events, might be suitable for expressing the law governing this kind of distribution. Substituting for the algebraic symbols in that formula certain characteristic quantities of the case under investigation, he calculated the frequencies in the various class intervals, according to that formula, and obtained the figures given in the third column of the above table. The conformity between observed and theoretical figures is so striking that it convinced scientists of the suitability of the formula for describing accident distributions.

Experience has shown that they were quite correct, and although the simple formula first used underwent several modifications according to the increased complexity of the data to which it was to be applied, we are still using to-day fundamentally the same idea and formula, and the whole complex of the mathematical forms employed is called the Statistical Theory of Accidents.*

We have to-day arrived at the theory that although an accident of a certain type, taken by itself, is something quite unpredictable because of the variety of causes involved, a great number of accidents can be transformed into a series which shows the working of the Law of Chance. It follows that, although we cannot predict whether or not a certain individual will meet with such an accident, we can predict how many space-time intervals, like Army Corps per year, will be affected —that is, affected with 0, 1, 2, etc., accidents of that kind over a great period of time, or, if we were dealing with minor accidents in a given occupation which could occur several times in one and the same person, how many persons there would be with no accident, one accident, two accidents, three accidents, etc., occurring to them over a given period of time.

* It owes its modern form to G. U. Yule and M. Greenwood

6.2 The Application to Industrial Control Inspection—Defectives as Accidents

How is that idea of regularity in the occurrence of accidents connected with industrial control ?

It comes into play whenever we are dealing with what is called " Go—No Go " gauging of a product. In this case we are not concerned with taking the exact measurements, but we put the article which we are examining for a certain characteristic through a gauge which is constructed according to the specifications laid down for that characteristic. The gauge has two parts. If the article fits into the " Go " part of the gauge it means that that characteristic does not transgress the upper specification. If it does not fit into the " No Go " part of the gauge—the " forbidden " part—it means that the characteristic is not below the lower tolerance. If these two conditions materialize, the article is satisfactory. If, however, it does not fit into the " Go " part, or does fit into the " No Go " part, then the dimensions of the characteristic are larger than admissible or smaller than admissible.

It is evident that one could construct and use " Go— No Go " gauges for characteristics which can be measured in the strict sense of the term. The gauges are then constructed according to the greatest and smallest measurements which are to be tolerated.

There are, however, cases of control inspection where the use of a gauge is the only possible way for controlling a given characteristic, and it is these cases to which the accident theory specially applies. If, for instance, we are dealing with the form of a somewhat complicated body, or with functioning defects, we cannot apply proper measuring instruments. The defect is here the result of a complex of causes, and materializes only if all these causes are present. If one or the other is missing the effect simply does not arise. There are thus no degrees of defectiveness in this case. The defect either exists or does not exist, and a third possibility is not given.

Let us, for instance, think of the form of a round of ammunition. Specifications are laid down for that form, so as to make it fit into the barrel of the gun from which it is fired. The only way of ascertaining whether the product complies with these specifications is to have a gauge available which imitates the dimensions of the barrel, and then try whether the round fits into that chamber, and if so, if it does not fall too short of the dimensions of that gauge. What this amounts to is to find out whether the round fits perfectly into the barrel.

In such a case it is not any more a question of chance causing a well-defined characteristic to deviate from the specification value to a greater or lesser degree, but of the combined effect of causes which, if the process is controlled properly, will produce a round of the right quality. There may be, however, comparatively rare cases in which all these very different causes combine, by pure chance, in such a way as to bring about a misfit, and such a combination is then quite in the nature of an accident. It either happens or does not happen, the first part of the alternative being comparatively rare. This is why in such cases it is conceivable to use the theory of accidents shortly outlined above, and it has been found in industrial practice that the theory is suitable for that purpose.

Although there are no degrees of accident as such, this alternative of presence or absence of a defect does not prevent us from drawing up a frequency distribution of samples according to the number of times a defect has occurred. For a product having a low average defectiveness, we will, as a rule, get a great number of samples (each consisting of a number of units) with no defects, and decreasingly smaller numbers of samples with 1, 2, 3, etc., defects.

6.3 Constructing the Quality Control Chart—The Meaning of the Control Limits

Having found that the number of defects in samples of a given size obeys a similar law as do industrial measurements— in fact, the law referred to as the Poisson Law, is very closely related to the Normal Law—it is but a small step to the idea of controlling the quality of a non-measurable characteristic by means of control charts of a type similar to that which we already know. These charts are sometimes referred to as Qualitative or Number Defective (Fraction Defective) charts to distinguish them from Quantitative or Measurement ones.

The usual practice in inspecting a product for a non-measurable characteristic is to take a fixed number of units, say 20 to 50, putting each through the "Go—No Go" gauge, and counting the number of either "Go" or "No Go" defects. If the characteristic was length of an article we would then get two distributions, one for the "Go" part and one for the "No Go" part of the gauge. If it was form of an article, we would, as a rule, get only one distribution, because in form gauging one is usually satisfied with the article fitting into the gauge, and the question of whether it fits too well into it does not always arise.

The sample quality is then recorded on the charts—one for each gauging characteristic—in the usual way. The left-hand side of the chart bears a scale starting at zero and progressing in steps of one, symbolizing the number of defects per sample of n units. The sample quality is then plotted by putting an asterisk (*) for the sample against the number of defects occurring in it.

The average defectiveness is easily found by adding all the defectives in, say, 50 samples, and dividing by the number of samples—that is, 50 in our case. It is this mean defectiveness of the product, as found from the samples, which allows us in a very simple way—according to the Poisson formula referred to above—to arrive at the 1 in 40 and 1 in 1000 limits. The meaning of these limits is fundamentally the same as described in Chapter II. They represent two (1·96 to be precise) times and three (3·09 to be precise) times, respectively, the standard deviation measured from the mean. But the standard deviation of a perfect Poisson distribution stands in a very simple relation to the mean : it is simply its square root. All we have to do, therefore, in order to find our limits, is to multiply the square root of the mean by 2 and 3, measure these distances from the mean in the positive direction, and draw horizontal lines at the nearest point of the left-hand scale for numbers of defects per sample * (Fig. 6.1, p. 145).

One difference from the ordinary chart is that the qualita-

---

* As in this type of distribution the mean and the standard deviation are no longer independent of one another, it is clear that only *one* chart will be needed for controlling both level and spread.

tive chart is a one-sided chart. It would be practically useless, although theoretically possible, to put the lower limits on the chart, especially if they are beyond zero. We therefore plot only one pair of the inner and outer control lines on the chart, namely, those which we obtain by *adding* two or three times the standard deviation to the mean.

As we are dealing with a one-sided distribution, the quantitative meaning of our control limits is somewhat modified. The 1 in 40 limit means in this case that there should be only 1 in 40 found beyond this limit in the whole distribution, whereas on the quantitative chart we expect 1 in 40 on each side of the mean to lie beyond that limit. The 1 in 40 limit, therefore, on the qualitative chart cuts off a percentage of the graph amounting, not to ·05, but to ·025. Similarly, the 1 in 1000 limit cuts off on the qualitative chart an area amounting to ·001, whereas on the quantitative chart the area of the graph lying beyond both 1 in 1000 limits is ·002 per cent.

The meaning of these limits is that if the defects in question occurred like accidents, on pure chance, with no disturbing factor intervening, we should expect only 1 sample in 40 approximately to lie beyond the inner and practically nothing to lie beyond the outer limit. To what extent this is met with in practice we shall see in paragraphs 6.6 to 6.7. But first a simplification of the method for constructing the 1 in 40 and 1 in 1000 lines will be briefly outlined.

6.4 Labour-saving Method for Obtaining the Control Limits

Although the arithmetical effort for constructing those lines is by no means great, it can be reduced still more by using what is known as the Poisson probability limit and charts constructed from it. In the chart, Appendix V, the Poisson probability limit is given in the form of a chart, from which for a given mean number of defectives we read the probability that a specified number of defectives *or more* will be found in the sample (chart, Appendix VA). Sometimes the probability scale on the left-hand side of the chart is turned upside-down. If so, the chart tells us that a specified number of defectives *or less* will be found in the sample (chart, Appendix VB).

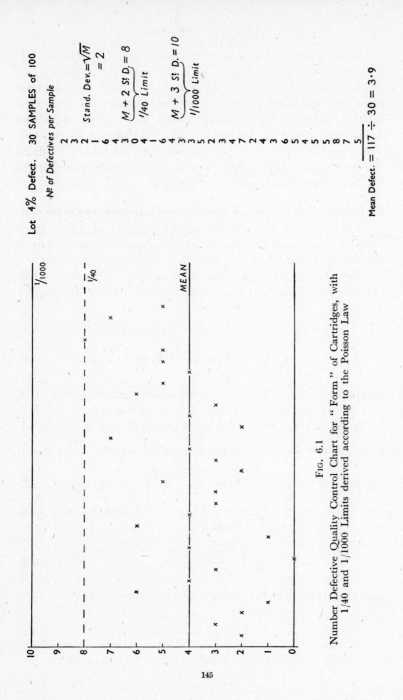

Lot 4% Defect.　30 SAMPLES of 100

Nº of Defectives per Sample

2
3
2
—
6
4
3
0
4
—
6
4
3
3
5
2
3
4
7
2
4
3
6
5
4
5
5
8
7
5
——
Mean Defect. = 117 ÷ 30 = 3·9

Stand. Dev. = √M̄ = 2

M + 2 St. D. = 8 } 1/40 Limit

M + 3 St. D. = 10 } 1/1000 Limit

FIG. 6.1

Number Defective Quality Control Chart for " Form " of Cartridges, with 1/40 and 1/1000 Limits derived according to the Poisson Law

From charts like these the diagram, Appendix VI, is constructed, which allows us at a glance, for a given mean defectiveness, (M), to read the 1 in 40 limit and the 1 in 1000 limit, by obtaining the crossing-point of the vertical erected at the observed mean defectiveness per sample with the 1 in 1000 and 1 in 40 curve, and projecting it to the left. There we read the number of defectives at which to draw the 1/40 and 1/1000 limits on our chart (sufficiently correct for defectiveness of less than 10 per cent.).

6.5 Computation of Limits if Defectiveness is Greater than 10 per cent.

This method for computing the position of the control lines—by means of the Poisson Law—should be used only if the defectiveness in the population is less than 10 per cent.

For greater defectiveness, the standard deviation is calculated according to the general formula for the Binomial * distribution

$$\sigma = \sqrt{npq} \text{ for Number defectives} \quad . \quad . \quad . \quad (6.1)$$

or
$$\sigma = \sqrt{\frac{pq}{n}} \text{ for Fraction defectives} \quad . \quad . \quad . \quad (6.2)$$

where q is the defectiveness, expressed as a fraction of 1, $p = 1 - q$, and n the number of items per sample.

As we do not, as a rule, know q exactly, we substitute for q the average defectiveness per individual sample, $\frac{m}{n}$ (m standing for the number of defectives), for p we substitute $\frac{n - m}{n}$, and write for the standard deviation of samples of n with regard to the number of defectives

$$\sigma = \sqrt{\frac{m(n - m)}{n}} \quad . \quad . \quad . \quad . \quad . \quad . \quad (6.3)$$

and with regard to the fraction defectiveness

$$\sigma = \sqrt{\frac{m(n - m)}{n^3}} \quad . \quad . \quad . \quad . \quad (6.4)$$

---

* For an explanation of this term see Chapter VII, paragraph 7.4

Two times and three times that quantity added to the average defectiveness in samples of n, then gives the 1/40 and 1/1000 limits, respectively.

6.6 The Distinction Between Statistical and Economic Control

The work with these control lines on qualitative charts is very similar to that with the control lines on quantitative charts, but there are important differences which must be observed if the product is to be effectively controlled, not only statistically but also economically. The differences arise from the fact that this time, on the qualitative chart for number defectiveness, we are plotting not averages, but single sample qualities. Consequently, the greater the sample size the more defectives will, as a rule, be gathered in a sample, and as the control limits are calculated from the sample quality, the wider will be the control limits. This is very different from the effect of increased sample size on our quantitative charts, where the control limits become narrower the greater the sample size, because the standard error of the mean, which forms the basis for arriving at these control limits, decreases in the ratio $1/\sqrt{n}$. This inconvenience can, however, be avoided by working with the fraction instead of the number defectiveness.

Furthermore, it is evident—and this the qualitative chart has in common with the quantitative range chart—that the worse the quality gets, the wider will be the control lines.

The consequence is that qualitative, like quantitative, control limits must never be used without taking into account what the economically desirable quality of the product should be. If it is desirable that the product should not be worse than say, 1 per cent. defective, then one must not be content with working to control limits which correspond to an average pefectiveness of significantly more than 1 per cent., assuming that if everything comes out within the control limits it will be all right. This would be a very wrong assumption. Let us make that point clear by referring to a matter which is familiar to everybody (Fig. 6.2).

An Insurance Company will calculate premiums according to the risk to be insured. The premium will be greater the greater the risk. To fix our ideas let us think of the number of

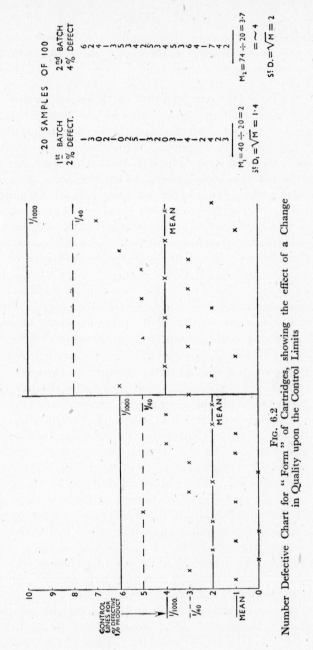

Fig. 6.2

Number Defective Chart for "Form" of Cartridges, showing the effect of a Change in Quality upon the Control Limits

20 SAMPLES OF 100

1st BATCH 2% DEFECT.	2nd BATCH 4% DEFECT
—	6
3	2
0	4
2	3
0	3
2	5
5	3
—	2
3	3
2	5
0	4
3	3
—	6
4	4
—	—
2	7
2	4
3	2

$M_1 = 40 \div 20 = 2$

$S^D D_1 = \sqrt{M} = 1 \cdot 4$

$M_2 = 74 \div 20 = 3 \cdot 7$

$= \sim 4$

$S^D D. = \sqrt{M} = 2$

CONTROL LINES FOR 1% DEFECTIVE PRODUCT

accidents for a given occupation or for a given period of life. The greater the danger of accidents in a given occupation, and the more exposed to dangers a certain period of life is, the higher will be the premium charged by the Insurance Company.

On the other hand, it is desirable to reduce the premium as much as possible, in order to make as many people as possible take out insurance policies without too great economic disadvantage for them. If the Insurance Company is to comply with this desideratum, it can do so only if the risk is reduced, that is, if the rate of accidents is lowered.

What corresponds on our charts to the premium—that is, to the way in which the Insurance Company tries to protect itself against possibilities of accidents—are the control lines. The greater the defectiveness of the product, and therefore the risk of defectives occurring, the wider will be the control lines. Too many defectives, however, would be just as undesirable as are too high premiums. Only a few people would take out insurances, and only a very small part of the product would pass final inspection, and a great effort would be wasted, in spite of everything being under statistical control.

The way out of the difficulty is to try to reduce the defectiveness in the product so as to make the manufacture of that product profitable. The indication that this ought to be done is given by comparing the actual position of the control lines with those which an economically fairly satisfactory product would yield. If the control lines are sensibly wider, then it is for the Production Engineer to do everything in his power to bring them to the level of the economically desirable control limits.

6.7 Working to a Target

Here again we must be on our guard not to confuse statistical limits with specifications.

Let us assume that a Production Management wanted to work to a target, that is, was aiming at a product with no more defectives than a certain amount, and let us assume that amount to be, say, 4 per cent. If samples of 50 are taken every half-hour we should expect about 2 in 50 to be defective. This would correspond to specification. From the chart,

11

Appendix VI, we read the inner and outer limits for this case as 6 and 8. But it is not these limits which should be put on the chart, once for all, although they may be put into the margin to remind us of the target. Whether or not a certain batch of the product complies with this target can only be ascertained by calculating the 1 in 40 and 1 in 1000 from the *actual* samples taken. The position of these actual control lines is then compared with the control lines for 4 per cent. defectiveness in samples of 50, namely, 6 and 8. If they are wider, the machine must be altered or other steps taken in order to make the product comply with the target.

But it would be a great mistake to put the target limits of 6 and 8 defectives on the chart and then work to these limits—that is, adjust the machine only when a point occurred outside one of these limits. The reason is this. It is true that if the average defectiveness in samples of 50 was 2, which amounts to 4 per cent., there would be very few outside the 6 and practically none outside the 8 limit. The converse, however, is not true, and this is where the method of fixed limits breaks down. If, namely, on a chart there are a few samples outside the inner limit and practically none beyond the outer limit of 8, it does not necessarily follow that the defectiveness of the lot is not more than 4 per cent. It is quite feasible that all the samples taken over a certain period will be round about, say, the 5 defectives line. According to the idea of working to the fixed limits, there would be no need for correcting the machine, because all the samples would be within the limits. But, as most of them would contain 5 defectives, the product would be approximately 10 per cent. defective. This case is illustrated in the right half of Fig. 6.3.

If the product is of great variability, then the use of the method of fixed limits is still more to be deprecated, because what it amounts to is that machines must be adjusted on the findings of single samples. A single sample, however, cannot be regarded as representative of the lot quality if the variability of machines or components is high. The proper statistical method, on the other hand, is better suited for such cases of great variability, because it does not work with single samples but by the combined results of, say, 20 to 50 samples. These

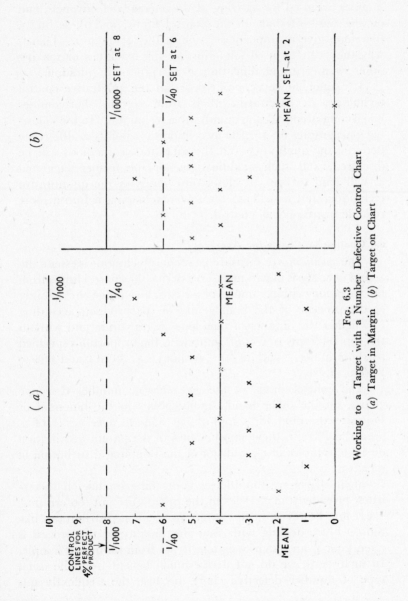

FIG. 6.3

Working to a Target with a Number Defective Control Chart
(a) Target in Margin (b) Target on Chart

samples are used for arriving at the average defectiveness, and
on the basis of that, at the control limits, and these limits,
therefore, give a proper indication of the lot quality. That is
why they can be used for adjusting the machines or making
other engineering modifications to the process in question.

It cannot, however, be denied that the qualitative control
technique, as described, suffers from certain shortcomings
when compared with the quantitative technique. In the following paragraphs 6.8 to 6.11 two important points of difference
between the qualitative and the quantitative methods will be
discussed, and such modifications for the former suggested
as will tend to bring it closer into line with the quantitative
technique, and as will go far towards making it into a more
reliable instrument of control.

6.8 Qualitative Charts for Averages

The *quantitative* or measurement chart technique is essentially
a kind of analysis of variance. We derive the control limits from
the variation within samples of n items, and judge the stability
of the process, or the homogenity of the product, according
to whether the number of sample averages within and without
the control limits is in conformity with the proportions specified
by those limits (" within " to " without " as 38 to 2 and 998 to
2, respectively).

The control limits of the *qualitative* or number defective
charts, on the other hand, signify points in the binomial or
Poisson expansion for samples (not sample averages !) of n'
items.*   That is, they signify values of the parent distribution
of single samples of n', and not of the sampling distribution of
means.

Such charts are suitable for controlling quality characteristics, provided the changes in the process are not too erratic.

It lies, however, in the nature of accident distributions like
those we are dealing with that the stability of the process is
often poor from batch to batch, if not from sample to sample,
In such cases, we do not derive much benefit from the usual
type of number defective chart, because the frequently un-

---

* We denote here the number of individual items per sample by n', to distinguish it from the number of such samples, n

accountable ups and downs of the control limits, calculated from a number of samples, do not allow us to improve the process for any sizable period of time. A machine adjustment indicated by one or a few " wilds " might not have the desired effect, because these outliers are just " wilds " and not indicative of the general quality level.

The way out of the difficulty is to bring the qualitative control technique more closely into line with the quantitative technique by obtaining limits, not for single samples of n', but for sample averages, and watch the distribution of such averages with regard to whether it complies with the proportions for " within " and " without " implied by the position of the limits.

In order to obtain such limits, we are making use of two properties of the Poisson expansion.

(1) The distribution of means of samples of n', picked at random from a Poisson population, follows the Poisson Law, just as the distribution of means in a normal population follows the Normal Law. But it is important to remember that the interval which in the parent Poisson distribution is unity changes in the sampling distribution of means to $\frac{1}{n}$ for samples of n.*

* Notes for the mathematical reader :

(1) If the general term of the parent Poisson distribution is $e^{-\lambda} \frac{\lambda^r}{r!}$, that of the sampling distribution of means is $e^{-n\lambda} \frac{(n\lambda)^r}{r!}$ the interval being $\frac{1}{n}$ instead of unity.

(2) If
$$u = \sqrt{(x)}$$
$$\delta u = \frac{\delta x}{2\sqrt{\mu}}$$
$$\text{Var}(u) = \frac{\text{Var}(x)}{4\mu} = \frac{1}{4}$$

(see J. O. Irwin, *Journal Royal Statistical Society*, vol. cxi, Part II, 1943).

For samples of n the interval becomes $\frac{1}{n}$, and we have

$$u = \sqrt{\frac{x}{n}} = \frac{1}{\sqrt{n}} \sqrt{x}$$

$$\frac{\delta u}{\delta x} = \frac{1}{2\sqrt{n}\sqrt{\mu}}$$

$$\text{Var}(u) = \frac{\text{Var}(x)}{4n \cdot \mu} = \frac{1}{4n}$$

(2) The computation of the limits can be very much simplified by making use of the remarkable property of the Poisson distribution according to which the square root of the variate has a variance which is almost independent of the mean, and is approximately constant, amounting to 0·25 times the interval. For the parent distribution, therefore, it is 0·25.

Considering now that the distribution of means obeys the Poisson Law (1), it follows that if we transform the distribution of means into that of the square root of means, its variance will also be approximately constant and equal to 0·25 times the interval $\frac{1}{n}$, and its standard deviation

$$\sigma_M = \sqrt{\frac{1}{4n}} = \frac{1}{2\sqrt{n}}$$

We would have obtained the same expression, $\frac{1}{2\sqrt{n}}$ had we calculated the standard error of the mean from the standard deviation of the $\sqrt{x}$ distribution for individuals according to the formula $\frac{\sigma}{\sqrt{n}}$. As $\sigma_{\sqrt{x}}^2$ is 0·25 (see paragraph (2) above), $\sigma_{\sqrt{x}} = \sqrt{0\cdot25} = 0\cdot5$, and the standard error is given by $\frac{\cdot5}{\sqrt{n}}$

Within the distance, then, of $\pm$ twice and $\pm$ three times that standard deviation, $\frac{1}{2\sqrt{n}}$, there will lie approximately 38 out of 40 and 998 out of 1000 averages respectively, provided the population is a simple Poisson distribution, that is, if the probability of a defective article remains the same throughout the process. A frequency of points beyond those limits in greater than the assigned proportions would point to lack of stability, or to a changing probability of defectiveness.

The use of the $\sqrt{x}$ distribution of means has been found very useful in cases which were intractable to the usual control method, and the removal of what appears at first sight only a lack of symmetry between the quantitative and the qualitative method of control has thus proved to be a real remedy.

6.9 Illustration of Usual Method When Applied to Mixed Lots

As an illustration of what has been set forth in the preceding paragraph, 6.8, let us take the following experiment.

Four lots of a mass-produced article (machine-gun ammunition) were selected which were known to be 3 per cent., 5 per cent., 7 per cent., and 10 per cent. defective, respectively, with regard to the quality characteristic " Form."

By means of tables of Random Numbers (see Chapter VIII, paragraph 8.6, for an explanation of such numbers) a scheme for obtaining a random sequence of samples from these lots was drawn up and samples of 20 picked at random from a lot, the lots being taken in the order of the random sampling plan (Table 6.1).

We denote the 10 per cent., 7 per cent., 5 per cent., 3 per cent. defective lots by A, B, C, D, respectively. Then the order of occurrences of these letters in the random sampling scheme can be taken to represent a random sequence of samples (of 20) picked at stated intervals from a product which is likely to vary abruptly. For each occurrence of the letter indicating a certain lot, two samples were taken, implying that the change in quality lasted for a certain short period of time.

In a case like this where the quality changes abruptly, that is, where it improves and deteriorates unaccountably in short bursts, there is little advantage in machine adjustments based on indications of a scanty changing quality level, because any such adjustment presupposes that one knows all about the cause of trouble and that the quality levels are more or less permanent, or at least that they can be maintained if satisfactory, and changed if not.

The following chart now shows the picture after 120 samples of 20 items each had been taken and limits calculated after every batch of twenty such samples (Fig. 6.4).

We see that no point falls outside even the inner limits, but that these limits move up and down, which would suggest that certain periods of production were consistently better than others.

We know, however, that this is not true for the product

TABLE 6.1

Col. I   Random Sampling Sequence (order in which samples are to be with-drawn from lots A, B, C, D)

Col. II   Sample Quality (in 2 samples of 20 taken from a lot indicated by Sampling Scheme)

The table shows how the lots are grouped in random blocks of four and of eight

I	II	I	II	I	II	I	II
A	3 / 3	C	0 / 0	C	1 / 0	B	1 / 2
C	1 / 0	D	1 / 0	C	1 / 2	D	0 / 2
D	0 / 0	D	1 / 2	D	0 / 1	C	1 / 1
C	2 / 2	D	1 / 0	A	2 / 2	B	1 / 1
D	1 / 1	C	0 / 1	A	0 / 2	A	1 / 3
C	0 / 1	C	2 / 1	C	0 / 0	D	1 / 0
B	1 / 2	C	1 / 0	C	3 / 1	A	3 / 2
A	1 / 1	D	1 / 0	C	0 / 2	D	1 / 1
D	0 / 1	A	2 / 1	B	2 / 3	A	2 / 1
C	1 / 1	A	5 / 0	D	0 / 1	B	2 / 1
C	0 / 1	A	5 / 2	B	1 / 1	B	2 / 0
D	0 / 1	A	1 / 3	C	2 / 1	B	0 / 2
B	0 / 2	B	0 / 1	C	2 / 0	B	3 / 1
B	1 / 1	D	0 / 1	A	4 / 3	B	2 / 2
		A	2 / 2	A	3 / 2	D	1 / 1
						A	2 / 4

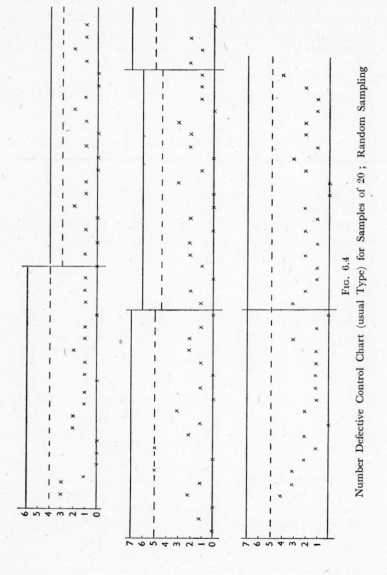

Fig. 6.4

Number Defective Control Chart (usual Type) for Samples of 20 ; Random Sampling

as a whole, because the random sampling scheme assures a reasonably even distribution of sampling over all the four lots, and these lots have always been " on tap " while the sampling was going on. This information, then, is somewhat misleading, and machine adjustments on the basis of the chart would not be justified. On the other hand, the chart fails to indicate the lack of stability within those " periods."

Now let us plot the number of defectives in samples of 20, if the samples come from one and the same lot in succession, but keeping to the order in which they actually occurred (Fig. 6.5). The physical interpretation is that the quality of the product was maintained at each of the four levels for a considerable time. (For order of samples, see Table 6.2.)

The first batch (coming from 10 per cent. defective lot A) shows the highest limits. The second batch (from 10 per cent. defective lot A and 7 per cent. defective lot B) shows an improvement. The limit lines for the third batch (mostly from lot B, some from C), however, have moved up, which suggests a deterioration of quality which is misleading. The fourth batch (from lot C, 5 per cent. defective) shows rightly a drop in the position of the limits. But the fifth (some from lot C, mostly from lot D, 3 per cent. defective) shows a rise of the limits, and thus again suggests a deterioration without a physical basis. The last batch (from lot D) has the lowest lines, in conformity with its quality level.

What must be inferred from this is that a machine adjustment suggested by the ups and downs of the limits will not always have the desired effect. It might even throw the process out of gear. For processes with the type of variability described above, we must modify our control chart technique.

6.10 Illustration of New Technique

Let us now treat the same sampling data according to the new method outlined in paragraph 6.8.

We first form samples of 4, as given by successive blocks of four values of our sampling scheme (see Table 6.1), and calculate their average defectiveness. We thus obtain the sample means of Table 6.3, column I, which are arranged into a frequency distribution in columns II and IV.

TABLE 6.2

Non-Random Sequence of Samples of 20 (but within each lot in the order of occurrence)

The Table shows how the lots are grouped in non-random blocks of four and of eight

A (10 %)	B (7 %)	C (5 %)	D (3 %)
3	1	1	0
3	2	0	0
1	0	2	1
1	2	2	1
2	1	0	0
1	1	1	1
5	0	1	0
0	1	1	1
5	2	0	1
2	3	1	0
1	1	0	1
3	1	0	2
2	1	0	1
2	2	1	0
2	1	2	1
2	1	1	0
0	2	1	0
2	1	0	1
4	2	1	0
3	1	0	1
3	2	1	0
2	0	2	1
1	0	0	0
3	2	0	2
3	3	3	1
2	1	1	0
2	2	0	1
4	2	2	1
—	—	2	1
		1	1
28	28	2	—
		0	30
		1	
		1	
		—	
		34	

The number at the foot of each column represents one sample number per lot

159

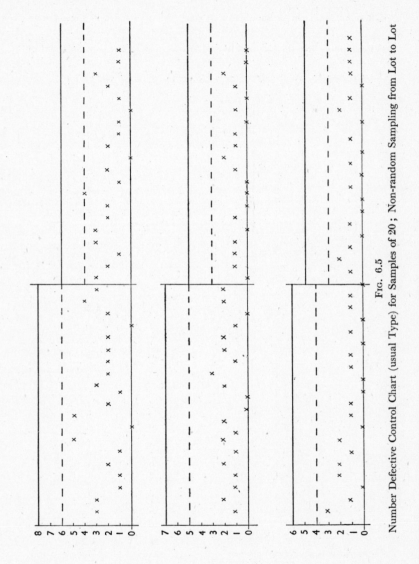

Fig. 6.5

Number Defective Control Chart (usual Type) for Samples of 20; Non-random Sampling from Lot to Lot

TABLE 6.3

Col. I Sample means of Random Blocks of 4 in the order in which they arose ($\bar{x}_i$)

Cols. II, III, IV, V Frequency distribution of sample means

I	II	III	IV	V
	$\bar{x}_i$	$\sqrt{x_i}$	f_i	$f_i\sqrt{\bar{x}_i}$
1·75	0	0	—	—
1·00				
·75	·25	·50	1	·50
1·25				
·75	·50	·75	3	2·13
·50				
1·00	·75	·87	3	2·61
·25				
1·00	1·00	1·00	8	8·00
1·00				
·50	1·25	1·12	5	5·60
2·00				
2·75	1·50	1·225	2	2·45
·50				
1·25	1·75	1·32	3	3·96
1·00				
1·50	2·00	1·414	3	4·24
1·00				
1·75	2·25	1·50	—	—
·75				
1·24	2·50	1·58	—	—
3·00				
1·25	2·75	1·66	1	1·66
1·00				
1·25	3·00	1·73	1	1·73
1·75				
1·40			30	32·88
1·50				
1·00				
2·00				
2·00				

$$M_{\sqrt{\bar{x}}} = 32 \cdot 88/30 = 1 \cdot 10$$

From cols. II, IV we get

$$\Sigma f_i \bar{x}_i = 38 \cdot 25$$
$$\text{and} \quad M_{\bar{x}_i} = 38 \cdot 25/30 = 1 \cdot 275$$

Now since $M_{\bar{x}} = \dfrac{\Sigma f_i (\sqrt{\bar{x}})^2}{30}$

$$\sigma^2_{\sqrt{\bar{x}}} = \frac{\Sigma f_i (\sqrt{\bar{x}})^2}{30} - \left(M_{\sqrt{\bar{x}}}\right)^2 = 1 \cdot 275 - 1 \cdot 21 = 0 \cdot 065$$
$$\text{and} \quad \sigma_{\sqrt{\bar{x}}} = 0 \cdot 255$$

Expected values : $\sigma^2_{\sqrt{\bar{x}}} = 0 \cdot 0625,$ $\sigma_{\sqrt{\bar{x}}} = 0 \cdot 25$

Similarly, for sample means of *non-random* blocks of 4 :

$$M_{\bar{x}} = 1 \cdot 275, \qquad M_{\sqrt{\bar{x}}} = 1 \cdot 08$$
$$\sigma^2_{\sqrt{\bar{x}}} = 1 \cdot 275 - 1 \cdot 17 = 0 \cdot 105$$
$$\sigma_{\sqrt{\bar{x}}} = \cdot 324$$

Next, the series of $\sqrt{\bar{x}}$ values is formed (column III), and their average $\overline{X}$ is calculated in the usual way, resulting as 1·10. The standard deviation for the $\sqrt{\bar{x}}$ distribution is then obtained according to the formula

$$\sqrt{\frac{\overline{\Sigma x}}{N} - \left(\frac{\Sigma\sqrt{\bar{x}}}{N}\right)^2} \text{ as } \sqrt{0·065} = 0·255.$$

First, compare how close this observed value of the variance is to the theoretical value of $\frac{1}{4} \times \frac{1}{n}$ or $0·25 \times 0·25 = 0·0625$. One might conceivably be surprised that this is the case, considering that our samples do not come from *one* but from different Poisson distributions, representing four different levels of probability for producing defectives. But let us remember that our method of sampling has to some extent restored the random element.*

It is, however, not the observed standard deviation but its theoretical value of 0·25 which we use, once for all, for arriving at the control limits for averages. We thus obtain the 1/40 and 1/1000 limits as $1·10 \pm 0·50$ and $1·10 \pm 0·75$ respectively. These limits fulfil the same purpose as the limits on the quantitative chart. They denote the width of variation for averages of n samples of n' specimen that will result by pure chance if the population is a simple Poisson distribution. Any excess in the number of averages beyond these lines indicates a disturbance or, as we say, lack of control.

The following figure shows the new chart for the distribution of $\sqrt{\bar{x}}$, or the square root of means of four successive samples of 20.

We find 3 averages out of 30 falling outside the 1/40 limits, which suggests lack of stability. This puts on record the erratic behaviour in short intervals, true to facts.

Now let us form the averages of samples of 4, if all four samples come from one and the same lot, taking the samples again in the order in which we happened to obtain them, but having first sorted the samples according to the lot from which they came (see Table 6.2).

* see Czuber, *Wahrscheinliskkeitslehre*, pp. 133–36

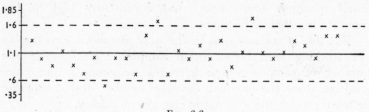

FIG. 6.6

FIG. 6.6

Number Defective Chart for the Square Root of Averages of 4 Samples
of 20 ; Random Sampling

The standard deviation of the $\sqrt{\bar{x}}$ distribution is now
somewhat higher (0·324), pointing clearly to the presence of
disturbing factors ; the chart (Fig. 6.7), with limits derived
from the theoretical standard error for a simple or undisturbed
Poisson distribution, shows again 3 points falling outside the
1/40 limits.

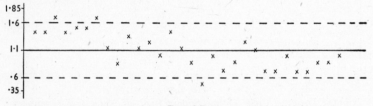

FIG. 6.7

Number Defective Chart for the Square Root of Averages of 4 Samples
of 20 ; Non-random Sampling

The impression we get from the charts for sample averages
is to some extent the reverse of that gained from the previous
charts for single samples.

There we got the impression of changes in the quality level
combined with stability or homogeneity within each of these
periods. *Here* we get the picture of a somewhat unstable process in the case of random sampling, or, in the non-random
chart as changing with the lot quality.

This is no doubt a nearer approach to truth, that is, to the
physical conditions, because, as we know, the samples do *not*
come from a homogeneous population. But it is still not what
we want, because even the new charts do not enable us to
distinguish between accidental variations, which ought not to

entail machine adjustments, and consistently bad quality necessitating such adjustments.

But this is not inherent in the new method. It is due to our working with rather small samples. The greater the number of samples whose averages we observe, the more sensitive does the method become to the vital distinction between erratic and systematic changes of quality.

Let us, therefore, collect the samples into groups of 8, first taking blocks of 8 from our random sequence, and then taking 8 samples from one and the same lot or from adjoining lots, in the order in which those samples have occurred (see Tables 6.1, 6.2). The following Table 6.4 and charts show the distribution of averages of 8, from the random sequence and the non-random sequence respectively.

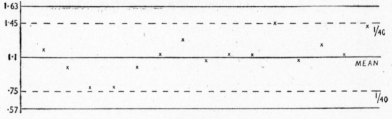

Fig. 6.8

Number Defective Chart for the Square Root of Averages of 8 Samples of 20 ; Random Sampling

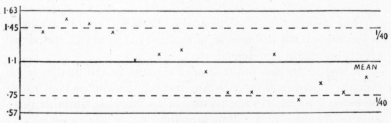

Fig. 6.9

Number Defective Chart for the Square Root of Averages of 8 Samples of 20 ; Non-random Sampling

These charts now give a definitely better picture of the actual physical conditions prevailing during the time of production covered by our sampling.

TABLE 6.4.

Col. I. Sample means of *Random* Blocks of 8 in the order in which they arose ($\bar{x}_i$)

Cols. II, III, IV, V. Frequency distribution of sample means.

I	II $\bar{x}_i$	III $\sqrt{\bar{x}_i}$	IV f_i	V $f_i\sqrt{\bar{x}_i}$
1·375				
	0	0	—	—
1·000				
	—	—		
·625	·625	·790	2	1·580
·525	·750	·866	—	—
1·000	·375	·935	—	—
1·250	1·000	1·000	2	2·000
1·625	1·125	1·061	2	2·122
1·125	1·250	1·118	4	4·472
1·250	1·375	1·172	1	1·172
1·250	1·500	1·225	1	1·225
2·125	1·625	1·272	1	1·272
1·125	1·750	1·323	—	—
1·500	1·875	1·469	—	—
1·250	2·000	1·414	1	1·414
2·000	2·125	1·457	1	1·457
			15	16·714

$$M_{\sqrt{\bar{x}}} = 16\cdot714/15 = 1\cdot114$$

From cols. II, IV :

$$\Sigma f_i \bar{x}_i = 19\cdot125$$

and

$$M_{\bar{x}} = 19\cdot125/15 = 1\cdot275$$

Now since

$$M_{\bar{x}} = \frac{\Sigma f_i (\sqrt{\bar{x}_i})^2}{15}$$

$$\sigma^2_{\sqrt{\bar{x}}} = \frac{\Sigma f_i (\sqrt{\bar{x}})^2}{15} - \left(M_{\sqrt{\bar{x}}}\right)^2 = 1\cdot275 - 1\cdot24 = 0\cdot035,$$

and

$$\sigma_{\sqrt{\bar{x}}} = 0\cdot187$$

Expected values :

$$\sigma^2_{\sqrt{\bar{x}}} = 0\cdot03125, \quad \sigma_{\sqrt{\bar{x}}} = 0\cdot177$$

Similarly, for sample means of *non-random* blocks of 8 :

$$M_{\bar{x}} = 1\cdot275 \quad M_{\sqrt{\bar{x}}} = 1\cdot10$$

$$\sigma^2_{\sqrt{\bar{x}}} = 1\cdot275 - 1\cdot21 = 0\cdot065$$

$$\sigma_{\sqrt{\bar{x}}} = 0\cdot255$$

The random chart, corresponding to a record of quality for a product improving and deteriorating by jumps which, according to the production engineer, must be considered "unaccountable" because of the complexity of interacting factors, and which, therefore, should not suggest the need for altering the machine or the operation, shows *none* of the averages falling beyond even the inner limits. The level of production seems maintained, as the same pair of limits serves for the whole.

The non-random chart, on the other hand, has three outliers : one from the best lot (D, 3 per cent. defective), which practically cannot be regarded as a "wild," since it occurs beyond the lower limit, and two from the worst (A, 10 per cent. defective), thus pointing clearly to where the trouble lies. The trend of quality is now quite unmistakable. Again, we have the advantage of being able to work to one and the same pair of statistical control limits throughout.

We are not any longer misled by the limits changing on account of *sample quality* only, and are thus in a position to differentiate between such *ephemeral changes* of sample quality and the more *permanent changes* in *lot quality*.

The limits on these charts were obtained from the constant standard error of the mean in samples of 8 in a simple—that is, undisturbed—Poisson distribution. That quantity is given by $\sqrt{\frac{1}{4} \times \frac{1}{8}} = 0 \cdot 177$. The observed standard deviation for the $\sqrt{\bar{x}}$ distribution of chart 6.8 (random sequence of averages) results as $\sqrt{0 \cdot 035} = 0 \cdot 187$, which is sufficiently close to the theoretical value to justify our assumption of a stable process.

The standard deviation of the $\sqrt{\bar{x}}$ distribution of chart 6.9 (non-random sequence of averages) is $\sqrt{0 \cdot 065} = 0 \cdot 255$, indicating disturbance, and thus confirming the conclusions reached by the control chart method. The control limits are the same as in the random sequence chart, because they are obtained from the constant value of the variance of the $\sqrt{\bar{x}}$ distribution for averages of 8 samples.

It emerges from these examples that the 1/40 limits are more sensitive to the distinction between stability and disturbance than the 1/1000 limits if we work with averages of samples of n' specimens.

The control limits being always at the same distance from the mean, it goes without saying that the question of economic control, that is, whether the quality of the product is as desired, must be decided solely by the position of the mean.

For the purpose of routine examination we cannot wait until we know the average for the whole, or a very long, period of manufacture. This would defeat the object of a synchronized check on the quality of the article as it leaves the production line. We therefore use in this case, to start with, as the mean from which to set out the control limits, the best attainable average quality of the characteristic in question, expressed as a number defectiveness.

6.11 Technique for Qualitative Charts if No Defectives are to be Tolerated *

(1) Another important difference between any type of qualitative chart and the quantitative one is this : working to control limits on a quantitative chart will, provided the limits are in the position required by specifications, result in a product free from rejects. With qualitative charts, on the other hand, no matter where the limits are which we obtain from the observations (excepting the case of the 1/1000 limit at zero), there will be a certain percentage of defective work included in the bulk of the product.

The reason is that only in the case where the average defectiveness in samples of n' is zero can we expect limits at 0, but whenever the average defectiveness in such samples is ever so small a fraction above 0, there will be 1/40 and 1/1000 limits at points of the scale appreciably higher than zero. This means that samples with a defectiveness not exceeding such limits will not lead to machine adjustments or other corrective measures. The result, then, will be the inclusion of a certain number of defective articles in the total product.

To summarize : limits other than at zero are essential for stabilizing or controlling the manufacturing process, and such limits imply the acceptance of a certain percentage of defective work.

(2) If it were essential, however, that no defective work

* see Dudding and Jennett, *Quality Control Chart Technique when Manufacturing to Specifications*, 1944

should leave the factory, then it would be necessary, and under certain conditions possible, to modify the basic method of control so as to achieve that aim. But here we must distinguish between low precision and high precision work. The first type includes processes with a high variability, the second processes with a small variability.

(*a*) For the first type there is no other way but to work to the quality control chart limits, either for single samples of n' or for averages of a number (n) of samples of n', keeping in mind a target of a very small percentage defectiveness (see paragraph 6.7), with subsequent 100 per cent. inspection and clearing out of defectives.

(*b*) If, however, the process was such that rejects could be avoided altogether provided sufficient care was taken, and if the characteristic was measurable, the following modification of the standard method should be adopted.

Its principle is this : limits or gauges are respectively set or made more severe than specifications demand. For instance, we make the size of limits or gauges such as to cause 10 per cent. of the satisfactory product according to the specifications *not* to pass the gauge or limit. The control lines are then obtained for such a mean " defectiveness " per sample of n' specimen as would correspond to 10 per cent. defectiveness in the total ; that is, we expect a sample of n' to contain $\dfrac{n'}{10}$ " defectives," admitting at the same time deviations from that mean value up the to control lines in decreasing proportions. The term " defective " is here understood as referring to the limits or gauges of increased severity, and not with regard to the specifications.

Working to these control limits, we can be satisfied that a stable process will mean that no part of the product is beyond specifications.

(3) To fix our ideas, let us think of the length of a certain article, say, metal rods, for which an upper tolerance—t_u— and a lower tolerance—t_l—are given, equidistant from a nominal dimension which we call the specification mean (M). Let us further suppose, in accordance with (*b*), that the process is capable of high precision work, that is, that the specifica-

tions can definitely be met in mass production, and that the characteristic is measurable.

We must first determine the size of the gauge or the limits to which to work (working limits in contradistinction to specification limits). We assume that the measurements will be distributed in accordance with the Normal Law, one tail representing " high " and the other " low " values. We know that in consequence of this (see Appendix I) the highest 10 per cent. of the product will lie beyond $+ 1\cdot28\sigma$ and the lowest 10 per cent. beyond $- 1\cdot28\sigma$ from the specification mean.

But, $1\cdot28\sigma = \dfrac{1\cdot28}{d_n} \ \bar{w}_n$ which, for samples of, say, 4, becomes $\dfrac{1\cdot28}{2\cdot06} \ \bar{w}_4 = \cdot62 \ \bar{w}_4.$

($\bar{w}_4$, or any other $\bar{w}_n$, is determined empirically in the usual way as the average range of, say, 20 to 50 samples of 4, or generally of n. This quantity, must be frequently checked, and the working limits altered if a significant change in $\bar{w}_n$ has occurred. It is obvious that gauges will be made according to severer limits only if one is satisfied that $\bar{w}_n$ remains, on the whole, constant and is equal to or less than $\dfrac{d_n(t_n - t_e)}{6}$.)

Setting out $\pm \cdot62\bar{w}_4$ from the specification mean, then, gives the limits—and the dimensions of the gauge—which will " reject," or not pass, 10 per cent. of the product on the high and 10 per cent. on the low side *if the total was within specifications.*

Working with samples of, say, 20 specimens, we now expect 10 per cent. defectiveness in the bulk according to our working limits (and gauges) for either aspect of length, and therefore 2 in 20 not to pass the " Go," and 2 in 20 not to pass the " No Go " part of the gauge.

We have to keep two charts, one for high, the other for low defectives, and examine each sample of 20 with regard to both characteristics. The sample quality is then plotted on the respective charts.

The 1/40 and 1/1000 limits for a mean defectiveness of 2 are, according to the Poisson summation, 5 and 7 respectively. These limits are put on each chart and remain the same throughout the manufacturing process. It is now these limits to which we work, and we can be confident that a stable process as governed by these limits will result in 100 per cent. perfect product, that is, product free from *real* rejects.

(4) For a process of very high precision, that is, with a practically constant and very small standard deviation, we can allow our safety limit to come nearer to the tolerances without incurring the risk of turning out bad work. The case is reminiscent of the modified technique for quantitative charts (see paragraph 2.11). The range $\bar{w}_n$ being smaller than it need be according to the distance $t_u - t_l$, we can allow the mean to vary more than would be accountable by mere fluctuations of sampling. This we achieve by *setting in from the tolerances* the distance corresponding to the $\bar{w}_n$ which resulted from our observations.

We know again that the lowest, 10 per cent. say, will lie beyond $- 1\cdot28\sigma_e$ from the extreme mean on the low, and the highest 10 per cent. beyond $+ 1\cdot28\sigma_e$ from the extreme mean on the high side. We do not know, however, the exact position of these extreme means. All we know is that they must be $3\cdot09\sigma_e$ distant from the respective tolerances if the product is still to be within specifications. That distance from the tolerance can then be obtained in the following way : the difference $3\cdot09\sigma_e - 1\cdot28\sigma_e = 1\cdot81\sigma_e$ represents the distance expressed as a multiple of σ_e, nearer than which no observation should approach a tolerance.

But
$$1\cdot81\sigma_e = \frac{1\cdot81}{d_n}\,\bar{w}_n,$$

or, for samples of, say, 4 :

$$= \frac{1\cdot81}{2\cdot06}\,\bar{w}_4 = \cdot88\,\bar{w}_4.$$

This quantity is now set in from each tolerance to give us the new limits or the new gauge dimensions. For each length aspect, high and low, we can again expect 10 per cent. "defectiveness" in the bulk according to these limits, and for samples of 20 we obtain the 1/40 and 1/1000 limits on each chart again as 5 and 7 respectively. These limits are then worked to in the same way as in the previous case, and with the same consequences.

CHAPTER VII

PROBABILITY OF CAUSES—STATISTICAL SAMPLING INSPECTION

7.1 Judging Lot from Sample Quality : How Not To Do It

THE sections on Quality Control proper—Chapters II and VI —were concerned with controlling the quality of the product during the process of manufacture. In the chapter on probability graphs, Chapter III, a method was given specially suited for examining incoming components, or for examining the finished product, if quantitative measuring of the product is feasible and advisable. As a rule, however, the inspection of the incoming components or the finished product is done in another and more accurate way.

As we know from Chapter VI, for measurable, or at least gaugeable, characteristics hand- or machine-gauges are used which will pass the product with regard to a certain characteristic only if the dimension of that characteristic is as the specification requires it to be. As a rule, the product must not be so great as not to fit into the gauge, and it must not be so small as to fit into the " forbidden " part of the gauge. For visual or functioning defects the product is subjected to a close visual scrutiny or to the " supreme " functioning test.

The method in use at present in industrial work consists in taking a sample of an arbitrary size (provided 100 per cent. testing is not made the rule), putting each item through the gauge, or otherwise ascertaining its quality, and taking the percentage of the failures in the sample to represent the percentage of failures in the lot. Let us assume that the lot contains 100,000 pieces, and that a sample of 50 is picked out and put through the gauge. If in the sample of 50, say, 1 defective is found, it is then reasoned that the lot of 100,000 is 2 per cent. defective.

7.2 Definiteness v. Correctness of Estimate

It is quite evident that this method ignores the influence of chance upon the sample quality. The smaller the sample size, the less likely is it that the sample quality represents the true lot quality.

Let us think of a great number of different lots of one and the same article, whose quality—as judged by the number of defectives—will naturally somewhat differ from one another. Let us further assume that samples of 100 are picked out from each lot, and the sample quality taken to represent exactly the lot quality. It can be safely stated that the conclusions reached in this way as to the quality of the respective lots will all be wrong, or at least the majority of them. This is the method which at present is actually in use in industrial sampling inspection.

But if, on the one hand, we must not identify sample with lot quality, so, on the other, it would not be of much use if we were to set out to find a method giving us complete certainty as to the lot quality if judged by that of a small sample. Whenever we judge lot quality from sample quality, we cannot do so with 100 per cent. confidence. If we wanted 100 per cent. confidence we would have to say that all these different lots may simply be anything between 0 to 100 per cent. defective, or very nearly so. Now, an answer of this kind, although theoretically quite correct, would be just as useless in practical work as the answer which is usually obtained is incorrect. In brief, the higher the correctness which is to be attained, the more details must be sacrificed, but this must not go so far as to render the answer useless.

All this points clearly to the desirability of having a method of obtaining the answer as to lot quality with a certain acceptable degree of probability. Is there such a method? It is clear that a positive answer can only be expected if we know the Law of Probability which connects lot and sample quality. In fact, we know that law, and we can derive from it the answer that if we pick a sample of a certain size from a lot of a given size and find so and so many defectives in the sample, then the probability is so and so much that the lot is of such and such a quality. We shall later use a more cautious wording so as not to clash with certain objections raised against what is called " Inverse Probability "—arguing from the sample to the population.

7.3 Demonstrating the Way in which Small Sample Quality will Deviate from that of the Lot

Before we consider the application of this law to industrial measurements, let us get a general idea of what it is like. An apparatus was constructed in the Ballistic Research Laboratory of the American Ordnance Department to demonstrate that *small samples showing a better quality than the lot of moderate defectiveness will be more frequent than samples showing a worse quality.*

To demonstrate this fact visually, a machine was constructed of which a sketch is given on page 174. The working of the machine is as follows. " The hopper of the machine is loaded with 900 copper-plated steel balls and 100 chromium-plated steel balls (the latter being regarded as defectives). The adjustable mechanism on the front of the machine is set for sample size 10, and a spectator is invited to operate the machine. The steel balls are continually agitated during sampling. The samples of 10 flow into the slot shown on the face of the machine. The operator can tell at a glance whether the sample is better than the lot (perfect), the same as the lot (1 defective in 10), or poorer than the lot (more than 1 defective in 10). By rotating the sampling disc, samples which are better than the lot are caused to flow into the right-hand test tube ; samples which are the same as the lot into the middle test tube ; and samples which are poorer than the lot into the left-hand test tube. The picture shows a typical run. Results are subject to sampling fluctuations, of course, and seldom are 35 per cent., 39 per cent., and 26 per cent.* ; but out of a great many runs, there has never been (and incidentally could not be) a case in which samples poorer than the lot exceeded samples better than the lot." (Simon, *An Engineer's Manual of Statistical Methods*, 1941.)

7.4 The Bernoullian Law of Chance : One " Cause " May Have Different " Effects "

In this case, only three qualities of sample were considered, but as a matter of fact, a sample of 10 as used in this case may have anything from 0 to 10 defectives, and we thus get 11 groups of sample quality. The distribution of these samples will

---

* This is the theoretical proportion of samples which are better than the lot, like the lot, and worse than the lot, respectively

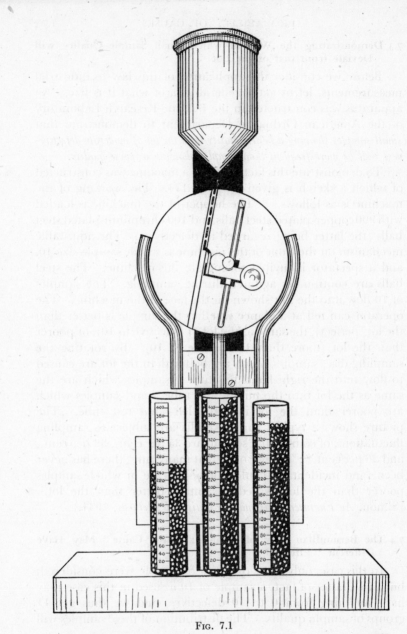

FIG. 7.1

Apparatus described by L. E. Simon in *An Engineer's Manual of Statistical Methods* (New York, 1941)

be roughly as follows : a high percentage will be just like the lot, a greater number of them will be slightly better than lot quality, and a somewhat smaller number slightly worse than lot quality. As the samples get increasingly worse or better than the lot quality they become correspondingly less frequent. This causes a distribution shaped very much like the one we know already—the normal distribution. It is sometimes called after its discoverer the Bernoullian Law, and after its mathematical structure the Binomial Law.*

Let us now see what the law is like numerically. The following experiment can easily be made.

We mix white and black steel balls having $\frac{1}{4}$ in. diameter in very great quantity, and make the mixture contain 50 per cent. white and 50 per cent. black. From that lot let us pick samples of 4. These sets of 4 can be of the following kinds :

> 4 white.
> 3 ,,   1 black
> 2 ,,   2 ,,
> 1 ,,   3 ,,
> 4 black

We may thus think of the lot quality as being a " cause " which can have not one but five different effects.

An experiment was carried out by picking 100 samples of 4 from the lot, and the following figures were obtained :

4 white	. . . .	.	4
3 ,, 1 black	. . . . .	.	30
2 ,, 2 ,,	. . . .	.	38
1 ,, 3 ,,	. . . .	.	20
4 black	. . . . . .	.	8

* If in the expression $(p + q)^n$, called a Binomial, p stands for the proportion of " successes," $q = 1 - p$ for the proportion of " failures " in the lot, and n for the sample size, then the probabilities of samples of n containing 0, 1, 2, . . . n " failures " are given by the successive terms of the expansion of the Binomial, $p^n + np^{n-1} q + \dfrac{n(n-1)}{2!} p^{n-2}q^2 + \ldots + q^n$.

A second experiment gave this series :

4 white	2
3 ,, 1 black	20
2 ,, 2 ,, ...	46
1 ,, 3 ,, ...	28
4 black	4

It is possible to calculate the frequency of each type of sample by means of the law referred to above,* and we then obtain the following smooth symmetrical series :

4 white	6
3 ,, 1 black	25
2 ,, 2 ,, ...	38
1 ,, 3 ,, ...	25
4 black	6

Although there are deviations between our observed series and the theoretical one, they are not so great as to obliterate the regularity due to the law, and they can easily be accounted for by

(a) the small number of samples (only 100). Had we taken about 10,000 samples of 4 we could have got a very good approximation to the theoretical series ; and

(b) by slightly irregular shapes of the steel balls, and possibly also by the arrangement which prevents complete randomness of sampling.

Now let us change the "cause" by mixing 40 per cent. blacks with 60 per cent. whites, and again picking a great number of samples of 4 and arranging them according to their quality. We then obtain by theory the following series, which can easily be checked by a suitable experiment :

4 white	13
3 ,, 1 black	35
2 ,, 2 ,, ...	35
1 ,, 3 ,, ...	15
4 black	2

* $100(\frac{1}{2} + \frac{1}{2})^4 = 100(\frac{1}{16} + \frac{4}{16} + \frac{6}{16} + \frac{4}{16} + \frac{1}{16}) = 6\cdot25 + 25 + 37\cdot5 + 25 + 6\cdot25$

We see that the percentage of the different sample qualities has changed, but the sample qualities as such have remained the same. We have again the same five types of sample quality or "effects" as above.

7.5 One "Effect" May Have Different "Causes"—The Probability of Causes

It is now easy to see how difficult it is to judge from any sample quality what the lot quality is like.

Let us pick out the sample quality 3 white, 1 black. If we obtained such a sample from a given lot, the lot could either be our first 50/50 lot or our second 40/60 lot, in fact, it could have come from a lot of any quality except one containing only whites or only blacks.

Just as one "cause" could have five different "effects," so one effect could have been produced by any of a great number of causes. What distinguishes all these possibilities from one another is only the different probabilities for a sample of a given quality to have come from lots of different quality. In our case, a sample of 3 white, 1 black, has the probability ·25 of having come from our first lot, and the probability ·35 of having come from our second lot.

This shows already the way towards solving our initial problem, namely, how to infer from a sample of a given size and a given quality the quality of the lot, with a certain acceptable amount of probability. From the quality of the sample we can determine the probability that a certain "cause" will have given rise to such a sample, even if we cannot directly estimate the probability of that "cause." Generally speaking the probability of a sample quality arising out of the various possible lot qualities will be a maximum for lots whose percentage defectiveness is nearly the same as that of the given sample. This fact forms the basis for judging lot quality from sample quality as it is generally practised. Nothing, however, justifies the expectation that the random sample taken should be just one of the most probable groups of samples. We neglect in this way the spread of sample qualities, or for a given sample, the spread of lot qualities that could give rise to such a sample. To make our estimate more true to facts the statement about the most probable " cause " should be supplemented by taking the spread of quality into account, and stating the range of lot quality from which with a high probability our sample could have arisen.

7.6 Simon's Charts—Description and Instructions for Their Use

If we had to carry out calculations of that kind it would take up too much of our time, and would also be too difficult, but fortunately the information which we want has been condensed into the form of charts. These charts have a twofold purpose. If we know the quality of the lot we can, from these charts, read quickly the range of quality we must expect in samples of a given size. On the other hand, if we know the quality of a sample of a given size we are able to infer from it the lot quality within certain limits, i.e. the range of the lots of different quality which with a certain stated amount of probability would give rise to such a sample quality.

Let us assume a lot of articles is inspected for a certain characteristic by taking a number of samples, say several hundred, and counting the number of defects in them—that is, the number of items in which the characteristic in question does not come up to specification.

To fix our ideas, let us think of a sample of 300 shell fuses, and let us assume that 6 defectives—that is, 6 fuses which did not fire—were found in it.

As a rule, and without using modern statistical methods, one would conclude that if a sample of 300 contains 6 defectives, and is therefore 2 per cent. defective, the lot must also be 2 per cent. defective. But this way of estimating the lot quality is quite wrong. It has already been mentioned that if we draw conclusions from sample quality as to lot quality, and if we want to come near the truth, the more definite and unequivocal we make our estimate, the further we shall be from the truth. If we want to get a really reliable estimate of the lot quality as judged from a comparatively small sample, we can do so only with a certain amount of probability. This is what Simon's charts * help us to do (see L. E. Simon, *An Engineer's Manual of Statistical Method*, New York, 1941).

* They are based upon a complicated function derived from the Bernoullian Law, and called the Incomplete β-Function Ratio

(a) *Inference of lot quality from sample.*—There are five charts from each of which to draw conclusions about the relation of lot and sample quality with different amounts of probability. We start with the chart marked " $I_Q = \cdot5$." * The horizontal scale gives the sample size, the vertical scale gives the lot quality, and the curves represent the number of defectives in a sample. Entering the chart with sample size 300, and projecting the crossing-point with the curve for 6 defectives to the left, we read a defectiveness of 2·2 per cent. This is in harmony with the fact pointed out above, that in comparatively small samples the lot quality will always appear a little better than it really is. It is important to realize that it is only with 50 per cent. probability that we can draw this conclusion about the lot being 2·2 per cent. defective. In other words, the chances are even of its being better or worse. But just because of this element of uncertainty, it comes much nearer to the truth than simply making the assumption that the lot quality is identical with the sample quality.

According to what was said above, if we want to come nearer to certainty, we must sacrifice some of the definiteness of information and accept a range of lot qualities, with regard to percentage defectiveness, within which the true value will lie. Such a range we obtain from the charts marked " $I_Q = \cdot1$ " and " $I_Q = \cdot9$." The general construction of the charts corresponds to that already explained for chart $I_Q = \cdot5$.

We enter chart " $I_Q = \cdot1$ " with sample size 300, and projecting the crossing-point with the curve for 6 defectives to the left, we read a defectiveness of ·013 or 1·3 per cent. This means that there is a probability of 90 per cent. that a sample of 300 with 6 defectives in it will come from a lot which is 1·3 per cent. defective or worse, and, conversely, that there is a 10 per cent. probability of the sample coming from a lot which is better than 1·3 per cent. defective.

Going over to chart " $I_Q = \cdot9$ " and proceeding in the same way as before—that is, entering the chart with sample size 300, projecting the crossing-point with the curve for 6 + 1 (*on this chart* !) defectives to the left, we read ·035 or 3·5 per cent.

* Appendix VII

defectiveness of the lot. This means there is a probability of 90 per cent. that a sample of this size and quality will come from a lot that is not worse than approximately 3·5 per cent. defective ; and conversely that there is a probability of 10 per cent. that the lot is worse.

It we wanted to obtain still higher certainty—that is, if we are not even satisfied with drawing our conclusion with 90 per cent. probability—we have to use the chart marked " $I_Q = ·005$ " and " $I_Q = ·995$," proceeding in the same way as before. We read on the chart " $I_Q = ·005$ " for a sample of 300 with 6 defectives in it, ·0095—that is, less than 1 per cent. defectiveness. This means that with a probability of 99·5 per cent. we can say that a sample of this size and quality will come from a lot which is worse than 1 per cent. defective ; and conversely that there is only a probability of $\frac{1}{2}$ per cent. that it will come from a lot much less than 1 per cent. defective.

On the chart $I_Q = ·995$, proceeding in the same way as before, we read a lot quality of 5 per cent. defectiveness. This means that with a probability of 99·5 per cent. a sample of this size and quality will come from a lot that is no worse than 5 per cent. defective ; and conversely that there is only $\frac{1}{2}$ per cent. probability that the lot will be worse.

We need not, however, draw our conclusions with such high probability as given by the last two charts. For practical purposes it is quite sufficient to work only with the ·5, ·1, and ·9 charts, and we then arrive for our sample at the conclusion that the lot quality is most probably 2·2 per cent. defective, with a possible range of from 1·3 to 3·5 per cent. (The probability of our sample coming from a lot of between 1·3 per cent. and 3·5 per cent. defectiveness is 80 per cent., according to how two probabilities are combined, viz. ·90 × ·90 = ·81.)

This information, although less definite than an absolute figure, is much more reliable and will, in the long run, fully justify itself.

(b) *Inference of range of sample quality from lot defectiveness.*— The charts are suitable for providing a second kind of information, which can be used for constructing a sort of quality control chart.

Supposing specifications were laid down for a certain

characteristic to the effect that a lot must not be worse than a stated amount of defectiveness with regard to that characteristic. To fix our ideas let us again work with a numerical example, and let us assume now that 2 per cent. defectiveness was the limit of acceptance with regard to that characteristic.

If we are faced with having to judge lot quality from sample quality, it is quite evident that the number of defectives for which to allow in the sample with regard to that acceptable amount of defectiveness of 2 per cent. will vary with the sample size, but the way in which they vary is not so simple as is usually assumed. We might be tempted to say that if the defectiveness in the lot should not be worse than 2 per cent., and if we were to take samples of 100, we might allow up to 2 defectives—or, in samples of 200, up to 4 defectives—but this would be wrong. We must again take the chances of sampling fully into account.

Let us assume samples of 400 were taken. How much should we allow them to differ in quality without suspecting the lot quality to be worse than 2 per cent. ? This is the fundamental problem.

Taking again the charts " $I_Q = \cdot 1$ " and " $I_Q = \cdot 9$," we can read these charts in an inverse way compared with what we did before. We again enter the chart " $I_Q = \cdot 9$ " with the sample size—this time 400—but now we determine the crossing-point with the horizontal line erected at the acceptable lot-defectiveness—that is, at $\cdot 02$, and the nearest curve to that crossing-point will give us the number of defectives to accept as a lower limit. In the given case we read 5 defectives.

This means that in a lot of 2 per cent. defectiveness we can, with 90 per cent. certainty, expect a sample of 400 to contain no less than 5 defectives ; and conversely that with a probability of 10 per cent. we can expect less than 5 defectives.

To obtain the upper limit of defectiveness we go to chart " $I_Q = \cdot 1$," and there we read for a sample size of 400 and lot defectiveness $\cdot 02$ an upper limit of sample defectives of 11.

This means that, with a certainty of 90 per cent., we can expect that a sample of 400 picked at random from a lot of 2 per cent. defectiveness will not contain more than 11 defectives ; and conversely that there is only a probability of 10 per cent. that it will contain more than 11 defectives.

13

(*c*) *Control charts for sampling inspection.*—This information can now be used for constructing a quality control chart for successive lot qualities. Let us assume we have sampled lot after lot by taking samples of 400 from each, counting the defectives with regard to our characteristic, and that the following series of sample qualities was obtained :

7, 8, 8, 5, 10, 8, 9, 10, 5, 6, 13, 11, 8, 8.

We could, of course, without any transformation into a control chart, see at once from Simon's chart that all samples except the one with 13 defectives could have arisen with a sufficiently high probability out of a lot which was no worse than the stated defectiveness of 2 per cent.

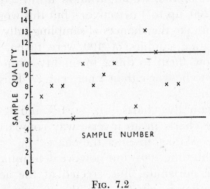

Fig. 7.2
Quality Control Chart for judging Stability or Otherwise of Lot Quality

There are, however, certain advantages in plotting the results in the form of a chart, especially as it enables one to discover trends which otherwise might escape attention.

To construct the chart, we mark the sequence of lots on the horizontal scale and the quality of the sample on the vertical scale. We then draw a line at 5 defectives as a lower limit, a line at 11 defectives as an upper limit, and now simply plot the sample quality by putting dots at the crossing-point of the ordinates for lot number and sample quality. We then see that sample number 11 points to a quality of the lot worse than acceptable.

This, however, does not mean, in the light of what we said above, that the lot must definitely be worse than 2 per cent.

It must be kept in mind that we draw our conclusions only with a certain amount of probability, however high. A lot outside the limits should therefore be subjected to a closer scrutiny before a final decision is reached.

It should be observed that the control lines on this chart correspond to different probability levels than do the control lines on the ordinary control chart. Simon's charts "$I_Q = \cdot 1$" and "$I_Q = \cdot 9$" allow us to draw conclusions with 90 per cent. probability each, that is, we draw with 90 per cent. probability the conclusion that a sample will be not worse than a certain amount of defectiveness, and we draw with 90 per cent. probability the conclusion that it will be no better than a certain amount of defectiveness. If now we want to obtain the probability that a sample will simultaneously comply with both these requirements, we have to multiply the probabilities in order to obtain the combined probability. $\cdot 90 \times \cdot 90 = \cdot 81$, approximately 80 per cent. It follows that the band on the control chart between our two lines represents 80 per cent. of our distribution of lot qualities, with 10 per cent. of the distribution lying beyond it on either side.

7.7 Tables Into Which Simon's Charts Have Been Condensed

These charts, however, may not always be available, and apart from this they may seem too intricate to the Production Man, who is not used to statistical reasoning or to reading charts of this kind.

I have therefore thought it advisable to condense the information derivable from them into tables, which allow us to read at a glance :

(1) the most probable lot quality for a given combination of sample size and defective number (Table 1, Appendix VIII) ;

(2) the lot quality range within which with a very high probability—80 per cent.—the true quality of the lot will lie for a given combination of sample size and number of defectives (Table 2, Appendix VIII) ;

(3) the range of sample quality (number of defects) we must

expect with a very high probability—80 per cent.—for a given combination of lot quality and sample size (Table 3, Appendix VIII).

7.8 Probability Graphs for Qualitative Sampling—Straight Line Graph for Poisson Distribution

The reader may have wondered whether the simple method of Probability Graphs, which we discussed in Chapter III for quantitative sampling, could not be used for discovering something about the " causes," in the sense of " lot quality " of qualitative, or number defective distributions. This is in fact the case. But there is this important distinction : whereas with normal probability graph paper stress was laid upon the graph providing information about the percentage of the product within specifications, and only secondarily about the nature of the distribution, it is just the opposite with qualitative probability graphs. Their foremost purpose is to provide information about the nature or type of the lot distribution.

The graph paper used for this purpose is the Poisson Summation Graph, Appendix V (A and B), and the method of constructing a particular graph is as follows :

The frequency distribution for the values of the variable 0, 1, 2, . . . n, that is, for samples with 0, 1, 2 . . . n defects, is summed, starting with the frequency of the highest (or lowest) class interval. This gives a series called the cumulative series, in which, if we started the summing at the highest value of the variable, the rth term (counting the frequency at 0 as the first term, that at 1 as the second, and so on) gives the frequency of samples having a value of $r - 1$ *or more*, and if we started at the lowest value of the variable, a series in which the rth term gives the frequency of samples having a value of $r - 1$ *or less* defectives

Reducing each integral frequency thus obtained to a total number of 100 samples gives the cumulative percentage series. These frequencies are now plotted on Poisson probability graph paper * at the crossing points of the horizontal at the

---

* Appendix VA, if summing from highest value, Appendix VB, if summing from lowest value

corresponding percentage (vertical scale) with the curve for the corresponding value of the variable.

The series need not be shifted by half an interval as in the case of quantitative distributions, because the scale of the variable is here discontinuous, and the distribution, therefore, not a grouped distribution.

If now the parent or lot distribution was of the Poisson type, and this it will be if the defectiveness is small (less than 10 per cent.), the crossing-points so determined will lie more or less on a vertical erected at the distribution mean. For example, let us assume that 100 samples of 100 articles each, say metal rods, were inspected with regard to whether the length of each rod did or did not exceed a specified amount, and were arranged according to sample quality as follows :

TABLE 7.1

No. of defects in samples of 100	Frequency of samples	Cumulative Percentage series
0	5	100
1	15	95
2	22	80
3	23	58
4	17	35
5	10	18
6	5	8
7	2	3
8	1	1

Mean $= 3$ $\qquad$ $\sigma = \sqrt{3}$

As the graph of the per cent. series shows (Fig. 7.3), the distribution of points is very well fitted by the vertical erected at the mean. From this we infer that the probability of a defective article is fairly constant, and that the lot can be regarded as being approximately 3 per cent. defective.

Looking at the graph, we see at a glance that an increase in sample size (say 150 instead of 100), will have no other effect than to shift the vertical line to the right, because in spite of an increase in mean defectiveness per sample, the character of the distribution has remained the same.

If our samples yield a distribution of points which can be satisfactorily fitted by such a vertical line, the type of control chart suitable for watching the *process* of manufacture is the usual type of number defective chart which, as we know, is based upon the Poisson Summation Function (paragraph 6.3).

7.9 Straight Line Graph for Binomial Distribution

The distribution of number defectiveness need not, however, follow the Poisson Law. It will not do so, for instance, if the defectiveness is comparatively high (greater than 10 per cent.), and the sample size small.

Let us assume we had inspected 100 samples of metal rods of 5 specimens each for length, and had found the following distribution of samples of 5 containing 0, 1, 2 . . . n defectives, that is, rods of incorrect length.

TABLE 7.2

No. of defectives in samples of 5	Frequency of samples of 5	Cumulative percentage series
0	33	100
1	41	67
2	20	26
3	5	6
4	1	1

Mean = 1 $\sigma = 0.9$

As shown in Fig. 7.4 the cumulative percentage series gives a straight line inclined to the left. This is the typical Poisson probability graph for the Binomial $(p + q)^n$, which, for our illustration becomes $(0.8 + 0.2)^5$. The probabilities of samples of n (5 in our case) of different quality are then given by the successive terms in the expansion of that Binomial.

If we wanted to control the process of manufacture, giving rise to a line inclined towards the left, by means of quality control charts, then the 1/40 and 1/1000 limits should not be calculated according to the Poisson Law as $\pm 2\sqrt{M}$ and $\pm 3\sqrt{M}$ respectively, but as $\pm 2\sqrt{\dfrac{m(n-m)}{n}}$ and $\pm 3\sqrt{\dfrac{m(n-m)}{n}}$ respectively (see paragraph 6.5).

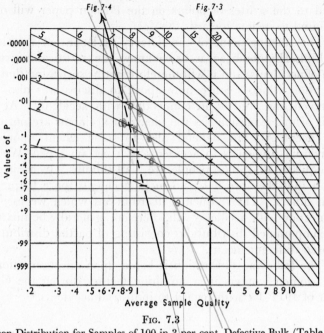

FIG. 7.3

Poisson Distribution for Samples of 100 in 3 per cent. Defective Bulk (Table 7.1)

FIG. 7.4

Binomial $(0.8 + 0.2)^5$ (Table 7.2)

7.10 Straight-Line Graphs for Compound Distributions

There is yet another typical probability graph which is of great importance.

A line inclined towards the *left* will as a rule result from machined characteristics, such as length or diameter of single components, if the defectiveness is greater than 10 per cent. and the sample size small. A *vertical* line will arise either from simple machined characteristics or for characteristics of assemblies of components, provided the defectiveness is small (less than 10 per cent.). If, however, the several machines, on which an article is turned out, differ significantly in precision with regard to the characteristic in question, or if the results of assembly processes are examined with regard to characteristics into which enter the qualities of various components, and if the percentage defectiveness is high, then the line which can be fitted to the scatter of points on the Poisson paper will often be found to incline towards the *right*.

The starting-point of the Theory of Repeated Events or Multiple Happenings was, as we know, the statistical investigation of accidents, and it will therefore not be surprising that the extension which we are now about to discuss was also first observed and studied in connection with accidents. At the basis of this extension lies the idea that accidents are not only just accidents, but depend also to some extent upon the individual proneness to accidents of a certain type. We say colloquially that some people are " all thumbs," by which we mean that they are liable to incur accidents more frequently than others. The frequency distributions which we meet in connection with accidents will, therefore, generally be mixtures or compounded distributions consisting of partial distributions around different means.

The following illustration is based upon an observation of 647 women workers in a munition factory during the Great War of 1914–18, with regard to industrial accidents.*

TABLE 7.3

No. of accidents	Observed frequency	Cumulative series	Cumulative %
0	447	647	100
1	132	200	31
2	42	68	11
3	21	26	4
4	3	5	1
5	2	2	—

Proceeding in the same way as before, that is, forming the cumulative per cent. series and plotting the results on probability graph paper, we find that the points can be satisfactorily fitted by a straight line inclined towards the right (Fig. 7.5a). Another distribution of this type is represented by the graph, Fig. 7.5b.

In industrial work, as observed above, we meet with this type of graph when the characteristic in question is of a complex

* Yule and Greenwood (1920), *J. Roy. Stat. Soc., 83,* 255

nature depending upon the qualities of several components plus the operation of the machine.

This is, for instance, true of the form of completed cartridges or "rounds." A run of 188 samples of 50 specimens each, inspected with regard to whether they fitted into the form gauge or not, gave the following distribution :

TABLE 7.4

No. of defectives in samples of 50	Frequency of samples observed	Cumulative series	Cumulative %
0	133	188	100
1	39	55	29
2	9	16	9
3	5	7	4
4	2	2	1

The cumulative percentage series plotted as before can again be fitted by a straight line inclined towards the right (Fig. 7.5c), which by chance is very close to that obtained from the accident distribution in Fig. 7.5a.

It is well worth noting that the differences between the pictures of our three typical lines has its exact parallel in the statistical differences between the three distributions. The *line inclined towards the left* represents a simple Binomial—that is, a population where defectives have a constant probability—q—and, therefore, successes a constant probability—p. The *vertical line* is the geometrical picture of a distribution which, although giving the outward appearance of a homogeneous distribution, that is, with constant p and q, is really a mixture of a number of distributions whose differences in means, however, are so small that they are swamped by the comparatively great variability within each distribution. And finally, the *line inclined towards the right* represents a mixture of distributions with significantly different means, that is, with differences between the various component distributions so great as to outweigh the variations within these distributions.*

* Note for the mathematical reader : This line is also algebraically the reverse of the line inclined towards the left because it can be interpreted as representing the Binomial with negative index. For instance, Fig. 7.5d is the probability graph for the expression $0.7^3 (1 - 0.3)^{-3}$.

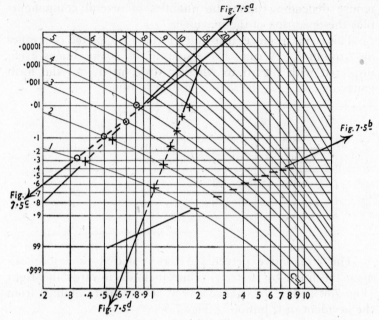

FIG. 7.5

Probability Graphs of Various Compound Poisson Distributions

7.5a   Compound accident distribution $M = \cdot47$, $\sigma = \cdot83$ (Table 7.3)
7.5b   Compound accident distribution $M = 4\cdot85$, $\sigma = 5\cdot7$
7.5c   Compound industrial distribution (Table 7.4)
7.5d   Binomial with negative index $0\cdot7^3(1 - 0\cdot3)^{-3}$

From the interpretation of the three types of straight-line graphs it is clear that there will be transitions between the three corresponding distributions. The graphs will in such cases often appear as lines curved to the right or to the left, and be of more or less irregular shape.*

Processes yielding a graph on Poisson paper, like Figs. 7.5a–d, cannot be satisfactorily controlled by the usual type of chart, and the technique outlined in paragraphs 6.8 to 6.10 is recommended.

---

* Yule (1910), *J. Roy. Stat. Soc.*, *73*, 26

7.11 Information to be Derived from Such Graphs

We now come to the practical purpose of such graphs. It is

(1) to get a picture of the nature of the distribution in the lot, especially whether the probability of a defective remains sensibly constant, or whether it varies from time to time or from machine to machine, or with any other criterion for sub-grouping. According to whether the graph is a line inclined towards the left, a vertical line, or a line inclined towards the right, we conclude that the probability of a defective remains constant, that its variability is negligible, or that it is significant ;

(2) to get an estimate of the defectiveness in the lot from which the samples were taken ;

(3) to enable us to estimate the proportion of samples of a given size suffering from a specified amount of defectiveness.

In order, however, that the graph should give useful information of this kind about the lot or population, we must first be in a position to know to what extent the sample can be identified with the lot with regard to quality. This reduces to the question of whether the straight line by which we have fitted a given scatter of points represents a " good fit." If so, both the nature of the lot distribution and the percentage defectiveness in the lot can be inferred from the graph. The problem is slightly different from one type of graph to the other.

(a) If the points lie more or less along a vertical line, the theoretical line is given by the vertical erected at the mean defectiveness of our sample. From that line, which represents the theoretical cumulative percentage series, we easily obtain the theoretical frequency distribution, and we then have two frequency distributions to compare with one another, the observed and the theoretical percentage series.

The comparison is carried out according to the Chi-square test (see paragraph 3.5).

(b) If the points lie along a line inclined towards the left, the obvious and most satisfactory way for constructing the theoretical line is to derive it from the expansion of the Binomial in question. For that purpose we would calculate the percentage defectiveness in our sample, regard that fraction as q, which at once gives p, and we could then set up the Binomial with the sample size, n, as index, whose expansion would give the successive terms of the theoretical frequency distribution (as fractions of unity). We could then proceed to compare the theoretical with the observed distribution (reduced to a total frequency of 100) by means of the χ^2-test.

But this procedure becomes laborious if the index of the Binomial is great, and it can therefore not be recommended for ordinary routine work. The only alternative is to draw the best fitting line to our scatter of points. From that best fitting line which represents the cumulative percentage series, we obtain easily the frequency distribution and have again two distributions, the observed (reduced to 100) and the "theoretical," to compare with one another according to the Chi-square test.

(c) If the scatter of points is along a line inclined towards the right, the satisfactory way of fitting a theoretical distribution to that scatter, and hereby finding the correct line representing the lot, would be to employ a function called after its discoverers the "Yule-Greenwood Curve," representing an infinitely compounded Poisson distribution. The comparison between the observed and the theoretical frequency distribution is then again carried out by means of the Chi-square test. As in the case of (b), however, the process involves somewhat heavy arithmetic, and it is recommended to draw the best fitting line free-hand and then proceed as in the alternative case for (b).

CHAPTER VIII

THE SHORTHAND OF INSPECTION—A RATIONAL SAMPLING SCHEME

8.1 Ascertaining Lot from Sample Quality as Distinct from Limiting the Consumer's and Producer's Risk—The Dodge-Romig Sampling Method

THE relation between lot and sample quality has been explained, and it has been shown how to make use of it in estimating lot quality from sample quality, and vice versa.

What emerged from this was that we could not have both definiteness and correctness of estimate at the same time. If we prefer to be correct in the long run, we had better sacrifice some of the definiteness and be content with a certain small range of lot quality. So long as this is understood and both producer and consumer agree—not upon a definite quality, but upon a range of such quality—there does not seem to be any further need for more complicated statistical procedures.

There is, however, something unsatisfactory about this way of making statistics the supreme arbiter for acceptance and rejection, and leaving it at that, since it unavoidably results in a certain small percentage of lots being wrongly classified. It has been rightly said by W. E. Deming : " There is no use in taking data, if you do not intend to do something about the source of the data."

We have seen how efficient statistics can be during manufacture, by firmly leading a more or less unstable process towards a state of control, and the question arises whether sampling inspection, too, could do more than " accept " or " reject."

As we shall see in this chapter, the answer is in the affirmative. It is possible by a judicious weeding out of defective work to do for the finished article very much the same as quality control does during the process of manufacture, viz. reduce the amount of defectiveness and ensure a stable quality in the outgoing product.

It must be kept in mind that, in using Simon's charts,

attention is primarily fixed upon the *quality* of the *individual lots* as judged by samples of *arbitrary size*. It is, then, either a case of ascertaining the lot quality from the sample quality, or of specifying the lot quality and accepting only such a range of defects in a sample of arbitrary size as is compatible with that pre-determined quality target.*

Very often, however, we are faced with the problem : " What *sample size* should one take ? " What is meant is evidently this : " What sample size is one to take if, *in the long run*, the consumer is to get what he wants, without exposing the producer to an undue risk of having good stuff rejected ? " Or briefly : " What is the most economical sample size compatible with safeguarding both consumer and producer against undue risks ? "

Schemes of that kind are available. Such a method does not primarily fix upon a certain quality of the individual lots, but aims at limiting the risks for both the consumer and the producer (if lot quality is estimated from that of a comparatively small sample) over a long period of time, or for a *very great number of lots* collectively. The standard method with these aims in view was developed in the Bell Telephone Company laboratories, U.S.A., and is, after its originators, called the Dodge-Romig method. We shall explain it in the following paragraphs, using the minimum amount of mathematics compatible with making the matter really understandable to the reader.

Paragraphs 8.5 to 8.8 give illustrations of how the method works and will, it is hoped, demonstrate the eminent practical advantages to be derived from it.

8.2 The Consumer's and Producer's Risk Explained

Let us assume that the consumer does not want to run a risk greater than 10 per cent. of accepting individual lots of a quality worse than a stated amount, and let that stated amount be, say, 3 per cent. This is called the *lot tolerance per cent. defectiveness*. What this stipulation on the part of the consumer amounts to is that he definitely wants to make sure that his

---

* For Simon's method of dealing with related lots (" Grand Lot System "), the reader is referred to Chapter VI, *loc. cit.*

risk of accepting a quality worse than 3 per cent. is less than 1 in 10, and that this risk will become increasingly small as the quality gets worse. In order to safeguard the consumer in this way, the following ideas are used.

We know that comparatively small samples from a lot of 3 per cent. defectiveness will have a fairly large range of defectiveness. According to their defectiveness they will have definite probabilities of occurrence. If the risk is to be 10 per cent., we ask ourselves what is the maximum defectiveness in samples of a certain size, if their number or frequency must not amount to more than 10 per cent. of all the samples of such size? Taking that maximum defectiveness as the border-line between acceptance and rejection will involve the consumer in accepting in the long run 10 per cent. of the product if it is not worse than 3 per cent. defective.

Now, it is evident that, if the defectiveness of the product increases, the percentage of samples with defects up to the number we have determined will become less, and this means that the consumer will be effectively protected according to his own stipulation, namely, that his risk of accepting a lot of a quality worse than 3 per cent. will be less than 10 per cent.

But this is only one side of the picture. We must also take into account the producer's standpoint, who does not want to have too many lots unnecessarily rejected for 100 per cent. inspection. By " unnecessarily rejected " is meant that he does not want to have lots rejected for bad quality if the average quality of his product has not deteriorated and is, on the whole, satisfactory to the consumer. This could happen if the comparatively small sample gave an unsatisfactory picture of the lot quality.

It is evident that as the consumer, for his own protection, draws the border-line between acceptance and rejection so as to accept only 10 per cent. of 3 per cent. defective stuff, and so rejects 90 per cent. of it, he will reject a certain smaller percentage of 2 per cent. defective, and a certain still smaller percentage of 1 per cent. defective lots, although 2 per cent. or 1 per cent. defectiveness might be perfectly acceptable to him. In this way the producer would suffer by having acceptable lots rejected.

The question now is how to combine the consumer's
protection with a reasonable safeguard for the producer, so as
to minimize the latter's risk of having good lots rejected.

Generally speaking, if the consumer wants to be protected
with a certain probability against accepting lots which are
worse than a stated amount of defectiveness, then the price
which the producer has to pay is that a certain percentage of
lots which are *not* worse than that stated defectiveness, will be
rejected, the percentage of such rejections getting smaller, the
better the lot quality.   The problem is how to make that
" price " a minimum.

How this is achieved by manipulating the sample size will
now be shown without mathematical formulæ.

8.3 Combining Both Standpoints

Let us assume that we are dealing with lots of 1000, that
the consumer wants to be protected against a risk greater than
10 per cent. of accepting individual lots which are worse than
3 per cent. defective, and that the *process average defectiveness*—
that is, the average defectiveness of the product during a long
period of manufacture, is ·45 per cent.

What is wanted is a combination of sample size n and
number of defects c, so that not only will the consumer be
protected according to his own wishes, but the producer's risk
will be minimized by a plan involving a minimum risk of
rejection.   As every rejected lot is to be 100 per cent. examined
by the producer and cleared of defectives, this is tantamount
to a plan involving a minimum amount of inspection.   What
we are aiming at is therefore that the number of lots which
are wrongly rejected for bad quality, and are therefore to be
100 per cent. inspected, shall be the smallest compatible with
the stated consumer's risk.

For a given defectiveness in the lot (3 per cent.), we can
easily arrive at a combination of n and c, so as to guarantee
that the consumer's risk of accepting a lot worse than 3 per
cent. defective will be smaller than 10 per cent.   For a sample
size of, say, 75, we get the mean defectiveness of samples of
such size by multiplying 75 with the defectiveness in the lot
—·03—which gives 2·25.   With that mean defectiveness

we now enter the Poisson probability chart (Appendix V) on the horizontal scale, and read that 10 per cent. of such samples will show no defects at all. The consumer will therefore accept the lot only if a sample of 75 is clear of defectives. Proceeding in the same way for $n = 125$, we read from the Poisson probability chart that 10 per cent. of such samples will contain 1 or less defectives. For $n = 170$ we proceed the same way, and read that there will be 10 per cent. of such samples with 2 defectives or less. We thus can get a number of co-ordinated n and c, so as to protect the consumer according to his stipulation, because if the lot quality gets worse, less than 10 per cent. of the samples will have a defectiveness equal to or lower than c, and so lead to more frequent rejection.

The question now is, which of these co-ordinated n and c will satisfy the producer by minimizing the risk of 100 per cent. inspection? The answer can again be obtained from the chart. In order to know what each of the sampling plans in the first and second column of the following table means for the producer, we calculate the mean defectiveness of samples of the size as stated in column 1 of table 8.1 for a product of ·45 per cent. *process average defectiveness.*

Doing this for the first sample of 75, we obtain the mean defectiveness by multiplying 75 by ·0045 = ·3375, and enter the Poisson probability chart with this figure as the mean on the horizontal scale. The crossing-point with the curve for zero defectiveness projected to the left gives the result that the probability of such samples appearing will be ·713. Using sample size 75 and allowable number of defects 0 as our sampling criterion, this means that of 1000 lots we shall accept 713 and consequently reject 287. These proportions, expressed as fractions of 1, represent respectively the probability of acceptance and of having to inspect a lot 100 per cent., and ·287 is therefore the producer's risk of having acceptable product rejected.

Proceeding in the same way for the following sample, $n = 125$ and $c = 1$, we obtain the mean defectiveness per sample of 125 items in the lot of ·45 per cent. defectiveness as ·55625. Entering the chart with ·556 as the mean defectiveness on the horizontal scale and projecting the crossing-point with the curve for one defective or less to the left, we read the probability of acceptance as ·891, and consequently a probability of rejection of ·109, and similarly for all the other combinations of n and c. The results are set out in columns 3 and 4 of the following table :

TABLE 8.1 *

n and c combinations for lot size 1,000, lot tol. % defec. 3% cons. risk 0·10		Application to product having process av. % def. − 0·45%				
Sample size n	Allowable defect number	Prob. of acceptance by sample	Prob. of inspecting remainder of lot (prod. risk)	Av. No. of pieces inspected per lot		
				sample	remainder of lot	Total
75	0	·713	·287	75	265	340
125	1	·891	·109	125	95	220
†170	† 2	†·958	†·042	†170	†35	†205
210	3	·984	·016	210	13	223
250	4	·994	·005	250	5	255
290	5	·998	·002	290	1	291
325	6	·999 +	·000 +	325	0	325

In order to determine which sampling plan involves the minimum amount of inspection, we proceed in this way. We must find out what is the average number of pieces inspected per lot of a given size. This average number will be composed of the number inspected in the sample plus the average number inspected in the remainder of the lot. The number in the sample is, of course, identical with the sample size. For the first combination of n and c it is 75. From a lot of 1,000 there remain, therefore, in the lot 925 pieces. In column 4 we see that of 1000 lots 287 will have to be 100 per cent. inspected. The average number of pieces inspected per lot remainder will therefore be $\dfrac{287 \times 925}{1000}$, which equals $\dfrac{265,475}{1000}$. Ignoring the decimals, we obtain 265 as the average number of pieces in-

* After Dodge-Romig, *Sampling Inspection Tables*, p. 8
† Plan involving minimum amount of inspection

spected in the remainder of the lot for this combination. The total number inspected is $75 + 265 = 340$.

In the same way we proceed for each combination of n and c. The results are entered in columns 5, 6, and 7 of the table. We see from it that the sampling plan $n = 170$, $c = 2$, involves the minimum amount of inspection, because the total average number of pieces inspected per lot is the smallest in the series.

8.4 The Dodge-Romig Tables and the Advantages to be Derived from Using the Method

In this way the first set of the Dodge-Romig Tables (SL tables) were constructed for certain ranges of lot sizes, lot tolerance, and process average defectiveness. From them such combinations of sample size and allowable defective number as will protect both the consumer and the producer, and reduce inspection labour to a minimum, can be read off at a glance for various lot sizes, lot tolerances, and process averages (see paragraph 8.5).

A second set of tables (DL) arranged in a completely analogous way gives the proper sample size and allowable defective numbers if the lot is given a second chance by taking a resample. An illustration of that procedure is given in paragraph 8.7. Specimens of these two kinds of tables are given in Appendix IXa, b.

The result of applying the Dodge-Romig method is that certain lots will be accepted on the strength of samples. Others will be rejected and 100 per cent. inspected. The first type of lot will naturally contain a certain amount of defectives, as only the defectives in the satisfactory samples will be removed. The second type of lot, however, will be completely cleared of defectives. It follows that the total, consisting of both types of lots, will be reduced in defectiveness compared with the total before inspection.

The Dodge-Romig method also enables us to predict the defectiveness in the outgoing total—that is, after inspection— and to adjust our sampling scheme so as to ensure that a stated amount of defectiveness will not be exceeded. In this respect, the method acts like an adjustable sieve for separating defective from good work.

Two parallel sets of tables, one for single sampling (SA), the other for double sampling (DA) allow us to read *n and c for a given limit of defectiveness in the outgoing total* (lots accepted by sample plus those which have been cleared of defects). (See conclusions to Tables 8.2, 8.4.) The SA tables are given in condensed form in Appendix IXc.

We thus find three prominent characteristics of the Dodge-Romig method :

(1) It works with sample sizes and allowable defect numbers which are calculated so as to protect both consumer and producer.

(2) It considerably reduces inspection labour.

(3) It enables us to set an upper limit of defectiveness after inspection—that is, in the outgoing total.

8.5 Illustration of the Scheme for Single Sampling—Demonstration of the Advantages to be Derived from It

Let us now check the correctness of the claims put forward by the Dodge-Romig method as regards effectiveness in

(1) Protecting the consumer ;

(2) Reducing inspection labour ;

(3) Limiting the defectiveness in the outgoing total.

This will also serve as an illustration of how the method is applied to actual conditions.

(*a*) For the purpose in view it is necessary to be in a position to compare the defectiveness of the product before inspection with that after inspection, and so to check the prediction made by theory. The *Universe* (this is the technical term for the total of the product) must therefore be completely known.

It is further desirable, in order to reproduce actual conditions of sampling as closely as possible, that human bias in dividing the universe into lots of varying degree of defectiveness should be excluded. That is, the number and distribution of defectives in a lot should be truly random. The way in which these conditions were fulfilled in the present experiment will be described in paragraph 8.6.

(*b*) Let there be given 25 boxes or linen bags containing

each 400 wooden or steel balls, representing a kind of industrial article, of which the percentage of defectives as shown in Table 8.2 is marked, say, red.

Supposing now that it was desirable to eliminate the defectiveness in the total formed by those lots. We could, without using statistical methods, do nothing but inspect all the 10,000 pieces individually and clear the lots of defective work. If we do that on a gauging machine we know that a certain percentage of wrongly classified articles is inevitable. If the examination is done by human examiners, errors are still more likely to creep in, especially if the inspection is visual and the examiners differ in their judgment of what constitutes an error. A certain small percentage of defects in the outgoing product is therefore inevitable, even with 100 per cent. inspection.

Realizing this, it would seem only sensible to accept beforehand a proper limit of defectiveness which can be made as small as desired, because by doing so we comply with one of the essential conditions for using such combinations of sample sizes and allowable defect number as will reduce inspection labour to a minimum. This will be seen from the conclusions to Tables 8.2 to 8.5, pages 203, 209, 213.

If, however, not complete elimination but only reduction of defectiveness was required, then it is evident that 100 per cent. inspection must result in waste of time and money.

(c) For the purpose of determining the quantities necessary for using the Dodge-Romig Tables a number of " lots " were inspected for defectiveness. It appeared at an average to be somewhat greater than 5 per cent. This gives a process average ($\bar{p}$) of ·05. As only a small number of lots were sampled for that purpose, the estimate must be regarded as tentative.

It was further assumed that the consumer wanted to exclude definitely the possibility of accepting individual lots with more than 10 per cent. defectiveness. This gives a lot tolerance defectiveness (p_t) of 10 per cent. Strictly speaking, the system does not protect the consumer in this respect absolutely, but only with 90 per cent. certainty.

The percentages of $\bar{p}$ and p_t are higher than those which

TABLE 8.2 *

Lot No.	No. of defectives			Total No. of defectives		% defectiveness
	In sample	In remainder		In lots accepted by sample	In lots 100% inspected	
		Accepted	100% inspected			
I	3	9		12		3·0
II	1	6		7		1·8
III	6	5		11		2·8
†(IV)	(7)		(11)		(18)	(4·5)
V	3	9		12		3·0
VI	3	10		11		2·8
VII	—	7		7		1·8
VIII	1	8		9		2·2
IX	5	12		17		4·2
X	3	11		14		3·5
XI	6	10		16		4·0
XII	4	20		24		6·0
XIII	6	17		23		5·8
†(XIV)	(9)		(19)		(28)	(7·0)
XV	4	7		11		2·8
XVI	6	16		22		5·5
XVII	2	25		27		6·8
†(XVIII)	(11)		(10)		(21)	(5·2)
XIX	4	14		18		4·5
†(XX)	(11)		(16)		(27)	6·8
†(XXI)	(21)		(55)		(76)	(19)
†(XXII)	(18)		(48)		(66)	(14)
†(XXIII)	(13)		(53)		(66)	(14)
†(XXIV)	(11)		(36)		(47)	(11·75)
†(XXV)	(13)		(38)		(51)	(12·75)
	169	186	286	241	400	
		641		641		

Of this total 55 occur in
not bracketed samples

* The number in front of the first vertical dividing line gives the number of defectives found in the sample, and that after the line gives the remaining number of defects in the lot. It goes without saying that in practical work the total defectiveness would be ascertained only in those lots which do not pass the sampling criterion.

† Lots IV, XIV, XVIII, XX, XXI–XXV to be 100 per cent. inspected

RESULTS

(1) Total No. of articles . . . . 10·000

Defects in samples of accepted lots 55

Defects in 100% inspected lots 400
___
Outgoing Total . . . . 9·545

Total number of defects in lots accepted by sample (after removing the defects found in those samples) 186

Defectiveness of total after inspection, including lots accepted by sample and those which were 100 per cent. inspected and cleared of defects . . . . $\frac{186}{9545} = 1·95\%$

(2) Total number of pieces inspected :   9 Lots × 400 = 3,600

                             16 Lots × 100 = 1,600
___
                                 5,200

That is, 52 per cent. *of* 10,000

Average number inspected per lot = 208 *approximately*

would be acceptable in practical work, because our lots showed a high defectiveness, according to what was chosen as constituting a defect.

The combination of the lot size N = 400, $\bar{p}$ = 5 per cent. approximately, and p_t = 10 per cent. allows us to calculate or read from the Dodge-Romig Tables a combination of sample size and allowable defect number, which will protect both consumer and producer and will moreover result in an appreciable reduction of defectiveness.

We read for those conditions from Table SL.10 * a sample size n = 100, and allowable number of defects c = 6, and a maximum defectiveness in the outgoing total of 2·9 per cent. We now sample lots I–XXV according to that combination of n and c by drawing samples of 100 from each lot and recording the number of defectives. A lot with more than 6 defectives in a sample of 100 must be 100 per cent. inspected and cleared of defectives. The result is set out in Table 8.2 opposite.

(d) Conclusions

We see from the above table that :

(1) None of the accepted lots was worse than 10 per cent. defective.

* For specimen table see Appendix IXa

(2) None of the lots which were more than 10 per cent. defective passed the criterion.

These two results show the efficiency of the sampling criterion, that is, the combination of sample sizes and allowable number of defects, in making the results comply with what we wanted at the outset.

(3) The number of inspected individual pieces is about half the total number of articles—5,200 instead of 10,000. This shows a great reduction in inspection labour as the result of applying a rational method of sampling.

(4) In spite of having thus reduced inspection labour by approximately one half, the fraction defectiveness of the product after inspection is less than 2 per cent., as against the defectiveness before inspection of 6.4 per cent. $\dfrac{641}{10,000}$.

It is also less than the acceptable limit of defectiveness after inspection, as given by the Dodge-Romig Table under the given conditions, viz. 2.9 per cent.

These results show that the predictions made by theory and the advantages promised by it are fully borne out by the experiment. Inspection labour and defectiveness of the product are both considerably reduced, and the defectiveness in the total after inspection is less than the predicted limit.

8.6 The Sampling Experiment on Tables of Random Sampling Numbers which Provided the Data for the Foregoing and the Following Illustrations

The story told in II is the translation into physical terms of what happened when 25 Tables of Random Numbers were sampled for four-figure sets containing zeros.

The reason for first constructing a kind of frame or skeleton for the actual experiment is indicated in paragraph 8.5 (a). Let us be a little more explicit about it.

Any sampling scheme is based upon the assumption that defectives will be randomly distributed in the total. In order, therefore, to reproduce actual conditions, we have to mix thoroughly the 400 balls which form a lot.

Now practical experiment has demonstrated that it is impossible to mix the balls or other objects so as to make their arrangement completely random. In whatever way we may attempt to achieve the result of a complete random distribution, human bias creeps in and disturbs the randomness apart from the disturbing factors due to lack of homogeneity among the objects. In short, balls or tickets or other objects fail in large-scale random tests ; it is as difficult to get artificially true random samples as it is to sample effectively a cargo of coal or barley (see Foreword to Tippett's *Random Number Tables*).

In our case the difficulty is increased by the experimental design according to which some of the lots are not significantly different in defectiveness. In such a case, the arbitrary differentiation between lots, by simply allocating different numbers of defectives to them, would be very unsatisfactory.

To overcome difficulties of that kind, K. Pearson suggested to L. H. C. Tippett that he should replace the whole system of tickets or balls by a single random system of numbers ranging from 0–10,000. In order to form such a table of random numbers, 40,000 digits were taken at random from census reports and combined by fours to give 10,000 numbers, which were arranged in twenty-five tables. Here is a specimen from one of Tippett's tables :

1596	3069	7906	6656	5298	5090	8580	6756
4951	6993	5243	6375	5088	2078	8339	0322
2876	0399	6741	2579	7552	4171	1364	9390
2670	7969	2909	8705	0188	9808	7206	8104
5808	4329	6681	9852	9458	0863	8491	1166
8298	1125	9153	9517	1481	0879	2355	2615
3117	0239	0770	8034	9978	9120	0967	0334
2385	1979	1120	3109	1169	0151	3869	3360
0039	4461	8674	5296	8111	5748	7451	2141
2400	4971	0464	1849	7055	3093	6860	7777

As a universe complying with strict experimental conditions of randomness, the 10,000 four-figure sets known as Tippett's Random Numbers (which form Tippett's Tables I–XXV, in No. XV of the " Tracts for Computors," Cambridge University Press) were therefore chosen. Each of the four-figure sets was taken to represent one observation and the occurrence of a zero in such a set as denoting a defective. A lot was taken to be formed by the 400 sets of four figures comprised in one table. This gave 25 lots.

In order to obtain a fairly wide range of variation of the lot fraction defectiveness, the number and position of zeros making a set of four digits a defective was varied.

For Tables I–X a defect was defined as the occurrence of two adjacent zeros in one four-figure set.

For Tables XI–XX a defect was defined as two zeros in any position, including the case of adjacent zeros.

For Tables XXI–XXV a defect was defined as one zero, not occurring either as the first or the last figure, excluding thus all sets with more than one zero and with zero at the extreme places.

From the lots I–X, XI–XX, and XXI–XXV a small number was selected and the number of defectives ascertained. From the results, which were weighted according to the number of tables of one and the same type of defectives, the fraction defectiveness representing the process average defectiveness ($\bar{p}$ in the Dodge-Romig's terminology) was determined. It resulted as somewhat over 5 per cent.

Putting the defectiveness which a consumer was willing to tolerate in an occasional single lot (but by no means in the grand total) as 10 per cent., we arrive by the D.R. Tables for lots of 400 specimens at a sample size of 100, and 6 as the allowable number of defectives, and this formed the sampling criterion for the experiment described in paragraph 8.5.

8.7 The Double Sampling Scheme Illustrated

(a) A modification of the Dodge-Romig system as explained above is the Double Sampling System. In double sampling the lot is given a second chance of acceptance if the first sample results are unfavourable. Other things being equal, the average amount of inspection for double sampling is less than for single sampling. On the other hand, the defectiveness in the total after inspection will be slightly greater.

The procedure is set out in the following table :

TABLE 8.3

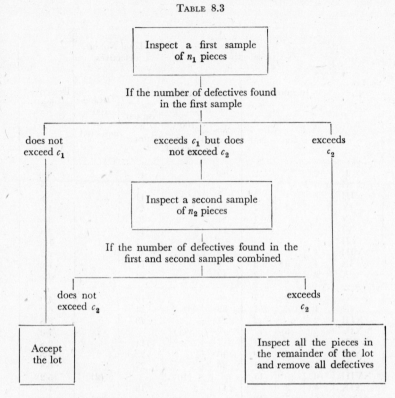

For our process average of slightly more than 5 per cent., a lot tolerance of 10 per cent., and lot size of 400, we find from Table D.L. 10.*

$$n_1 = 60 \qquad c_1 = 2$$
$$n_2 = 90$$
$$n_1 \text{ and } n_2 = 150 \qquad c_2 = 10$$

Upper limit of defectiveness in outgoing total : 3·2 per cent.

For a sample of 60, the first 60 sets of four figures of each table were chosen, for the additional sample of 90 the following 90 four-figure sets. The results are set out in Table 8.4, which is arranged like Table 8.2.

* For specimen table see Appendix IXb

TABLE 8.4

Lot No.	No. of defectives					Total No. of defectives		Defectiveness
	In sample			In remainder		In lots accepted by sample	In lots 100% inspected	
	1st	2nd	1st + 2nd	Accepted	100% inspected			
I	12	—	2	10		12		3·0
II	—		—	7		7		1·8
III	3	4	7	4		11		2·8
IV	3	4	7	11		18		4·5
V	1		1	11		12		3·0
VI	—		—	11		11		2·8
VII	—		—	7		7		1·8
VIII	1		1	8		9		2·2
IX	4	5	9	8		17		4·2
X	2		2	12		14		3·5
XI	4	3	7	9		16		4·0
XII	1		1	23		24		6·0
XIII	2		2	21		23		5·8
*(XIV)	(5)	(6)	(11)		(17)		(28)	(7·0)
XV	3	1	4	7		11		2·8
XVI	5	4	9	13		22		5·5
XVII	1		1	26		27		6·8
*(XVIII)	(6)	(5)	(11)		(10)		(21)	(5·2)
XIX	4	3	7	11		18		4·5
*(XX)	(6)	(7)	(13)		(14)		(27)	(6·8)
*(XXI)	(10)	(19)	(29)		(47)		(76)	(19)
*(XXII)	(12)		(12)		(54)		(66)	(14)
*(XXIII)	(7)	(10)	(17)		(49)		(66)	(14)
*(XXIV)	(8)	(7)	(15)		(32)		(47)	(11·75)
*(XXV)	(7)	(14)	(21)		(30)		(51)	(12·75)
			189	199	253	259	382	

641   641

Of this total 60 occur in
not bracketed samples

* Lots XIV, XVIII, XX, XXI–XXV were 100 per cent. inspected

RESULTS

(1) Total number of articles 10,000

Defectives in samples of accepted lots 60

Defectives in 100 per cent. inspected lots 382

―――――

Outgoing Total 9,558

Total number of defects in lots accepted by sample—that is, after removing the defects found in the samples 199

Defectiveness of total after inspection, including both lots accepted by sample and such as were 100 per cent. inspected and cleared of defectives . . . . $\frac{199}{9558}$ = 2·08%

(2) Total number of pieces inspected

$$
\begin{array}{llr}
10 \text{ Lots} \times 60 \text{ (only 1st sample)} & = & 600 \\
7 \text{ Lots} \times 150 \text{ (1st and 2nd samples)} & = & 1,050 \\
8 \text{ Lots} \times 400 \text{ (100 per cent.)} & = & 3,200 \\
\end{array}
$$

―――――

4,850

That is, 48·5 per cent. of 10,000
Average number of pieces inspected per lot = 194

(b) *Conclusions.*

From results (1) and (2) in the above table we see that double sampling works in principle like single sampling. It will materially reduce inspection labour and safeguard against the defectiveness in the outgoing total product exceeding a stated acceptable amount.

Furthermore, comparing results (1) and (2) of the above tables, we find that the predictions made by theory about the difference between single and double sampling with regard to the number of inspected pieces, and the defectiveness after inspection (see section (a) of this paragraph) are borne out by the experiment :

Sampling method	Number of inspected pieces	Average defectiveness in total after inspection	
		Found	Limit
S.S.	5,200	1·95%	2·9%
D.S.	4,850	2·08%	3·2%

We need not be deterred by these high percentages of defectiveness in the outgoing product. They are the consequences of the high defectiveness in the product before inspection. For a product of moderate defectiveness of, say, up to 2–3 per cent. we can get for lots of 400 a limit in the outgoing product of between ·82 per cent. and 1·1 per cent. only, and the actual defectiveness after inspection will, in most cases, be well below these limits. The result would thus not be materially different from what we could reasonably hope to get by 100 per cent. inspection.

8.8 Modification of the Original Dodge-Romig System if the Article is Inspected for a Number of Defects Simultaneously

(a) Sometimes inspection is extended to a group of characteristics instead of to one characteristic only. Provided that the defects with respect to these characteristics are of the same seriousness, and may be considered additive, the Dodge-Romig method—with some modifications—can be applied to this kind of inspection.

This extension is envisaged by Dodge-Romig on page 14 of their article in Volume 20 of the *Bell System Technical Journal*, and so far they are right. They do not seem, however, to appreciate the changes that become necessary with regard to what is now to be considered the " lot " and the " sample." The lot size, in this case, is no longer given by the number of pieces, neither is the sample size.

Supposing we were inspecting for four types of defects. Then a total of, say, 10,000 pieces, represents $4 \times 10,000$ opportunities for defects, either occurring or not occurring. More precisely, our universe consists no longer of 10,000 pieces as before, but of 40,000 loci—that is, potential places for defects, or freedom from such. We can also think of so many holes, into which the defects fit like pegs. A hole without a peg is then considered as not defective. A " lot " is now a lot of such loci. A lot of, say, 400 pieces would represent a lot of $4 \times 400 = 1600$ observations. This is the lot size with which to enter the Dodge-Romig Tables. Similarly, the sample size n means n loci. As we cannot work with a fixed number of loci, but only with a fixed number of specimens, we must necessarily pick a sample of pieces whose size is obtained by dividing the number given by the Dodge-Romig Tables by the number of types of defects, four in our case. The letter c is now the number of defects, not " defectives," which is allowed to occur in the sample of n divided by 4. For our lots of 400 pieces, that is, 1600 individual potential places for defects, we now read

$$n = 195 \qquad c = 14$$

that is, we have to pick samples of n divided by 4, that is, $\frac{195}{4}$ $= 48 \cdot 75$. We thus pick a sample of 49 and count the number of all the four types of defects occurring in them, passing up to 14.

(*b*) Turning to our experimental frame, we have to modify our criterion for defectiveness. We regard a set of four figures as one piece and let the occurrence of 1 mark the article as defective. According to the place in which a 1 occurs, a different type of defectiveness is indicated. We may thus get sets of four, with 0, 1, 2, 3, or 4 defectives in them.

As the percentage of four-figure sets with 1 in them is considerable, it was thought fit to reduce the defectiveness in some of the lots by regarding certain rows of figures as being free of defects, which served at the same time as a means for varying the lot defectiveness.

Thus, for Lots I–X, defects were not counted in rows 1, 2, and 3, that is, these rows were considered as not containing any defects.

For Lots XI–XV defects were not counted in rows, 1, 2, 3, and 4.

Lots XVI–XX defects were not counted in rows 1, 2, 3, 4, and 5.

In Lots XXI–XXV defects were counted in all rows.

The results are exhibited in the following Table 8.5.

Table 8.5

Lot No.	No. of defects			Total No. of defects	
	In sample	In remainder		In lots accepted by sample	In lots 100% inspected
		Accepted	100% inspected		
(I)	(17)		118		135
(II)	(16)		92		108
(III)	(19)		111		130
IV	11	97		108	
V	12	97		109	
VI	14	94		108	
(VII)	(17)		92		109
VIII	9	98		107	
IX	8	111		119	
X	14	87		101	
(XI)	(15)		87		102
XII	12	73		85	
XIII	10	77		87	
(XIV)	(17)		75		92
XV	7	98		105	
XVI	12	64		76	
XVII	13	90		103	
XVIII	10	71		81	
XIX	9	71		80	
XX	11	66		77	
(XXI)	(17)		117		134
XXII	8	151		159	
(XXIII)	(25)		128		153
(XXIV)	(19)		152		171
(XXV)	(22)		136		158
	344	1345	1108	1505	1292
		2797		2797	

Of this total 160 occur in not bracketed samples

RESULTS

(1) Total number of occasions for defects 40,000
Defects in samples of accepted lots 160
Defects in 100 per cent. inspected lots 1,292

Outgoing Total 38,548
Total number of defects after inspection 1,345
Defectiveness of total . . . . . $\frac{1345}{38548} = 3 \cdot 5\%$
Defectives before inspection $\frac{2797}{40000} = 7\%$ approx.

(2) Total number of inspection incidents :

$$10 \text{ Lots } 100\% \qquad 10 \times 1{,}600 = 16{,}000$$
$$15 \text{ Lots by sample } 15 \times \quad 195 = 2{,}925$$

$$18{,}925$$

Total number of pieces inspected = 18,925 : 4 = 4,731
That is, little more than 47 per cent. of the 10,000 articles contained in the 15 lots.
Average number of pieces inspected per lot = 190 *approximately.*

(*c*) From results (1) and (2) we see that the predictions made by the theory are again borne out by experiment.

(*a*) Number of pieces inspected is less than half the total number —4,731.

(*b*) The defectiveness in the outgoing total is 3·5 per cent., against the defectiveness before inspection of nearly 7 per cent., and is less than the limit of defectiveness given in the Dodge-Romig Tables under the given conditions, namely, 4·4 per cent.

It appears, therefore, that the method is equally suitable in the case of simultaneous inspection for a number of defects, provided the necessary modifications are made.

8.9 The Shorthand Method of Inspection

The rational sampling scheme enables us to determine the defectiveness in the outgoing total with great accuracy by choosing such a combination of *n* and *c* as will under the given conditions reduce the existing defectiveness below a stated limit.

The consequence is that we know the quality of the outgoing total just as well, if not better, than if we had tested everything. We have been spared that trouble and have had to test only a fraction, say less than 50 per cent. in our examples.

Our knowledge of the quality of the product over a long

period of time has thus been achieved with a considerable saving of labour. The principle of reconstructing the picture of the total from the disconnected data provided by our sample, according to a rational procedure, reminds one forcibly of that involved in shorthand. There we reconstruct the longhand text from the disconnected shorthand notes, by recognized rules.

In a certain sense, all quality control by statistical methods can be conceived as resting upon the same principle. Our aim is always the determination of the quality of the total product from that found in disconnected samples, and the procedure which is to be observed if the estimate is to be reliable is based upon what we know about the statistical relationship between lot and sample quality.

In the light of this analogue it becomes clear what an arbitrary sampling criterion—say 100 with no defectives among them—or any arbitrary method of judging lot by sample quality, means. It is as if every shorthand typist were to rely on his or her ingenuity in abbreviating or condensing the longhand text, and, consequently also on his or her intuition when it comes to reconstructing that text. Such procedure can have satisfactory results only in very exceptional cases, and it would therefore seem good sense to adhere to the recognized method there, and to the rational method in our case of industrial control of quality.

But quality control does more than merely determine the quality of the product, in the sense of registering its changes during production or at inspection. In using statistical methods, we *actively* determine the quality by aiming at a stable process within specifications—during the process of manufacture—and by aiming at a stable quality of the outgoing product compatible with the requirements of both consumer and producer—in the inspection stage. This constitutes the characteristic feature of what we may call " Dynamic Statistics."

APPENDICES

APPENDIX I

This table gives the Probability P, of an Observation falling outside the Limits $\pm \frac{x}{\sigma}$, where x is the Deviation from the Mean and σ the Standard Deviation.

For the Cumulative (" Ogive ") Curve, the Proportion of the whole area of the Normal Curve lying to the right of $+ \frac{x}{\sigma}$ is given by $\frac{P}{2}$, and that to the left of $+ \frac{x}{\sigma}$ by $1 - \frac{P}{2}$.

x/σ	P	x/σ	P
0·0	1·000	2·1	·036
0·1	·920	2·2	·028
0·2	·842	2·3	·022
0·3	·764	2·4	·016
0·4	·689	2·5	·012
0·5	·617	2·6	·009
0·6	·549	2·7	·007
0·7	·484	2·8	·005
0·8	·424	2·9	·004
0·9	·368	3·0	·003
1·0	·317	3·1	·002
1·1	·271	3·2	·0014
1·2	·230	3·3	·001
1·3	·194	3·4	·0007
1·4	·162	3·5	·0005
1·5	·134	3·6	·0003
1·6	·110	3·7	·0002
1·7	·089	3·8	·00014
1·8	·072	3·9	·0001
1·9	·057	4·0	·00006
2·0	·046		

APPENDIX II

Instructions for Calculating the Mean and Standard Deviation

(1) The most natural step in reducing a series of measurements to a more compact form is to find their average, i.e. to add the observations and divide by the number of items. This provides a single figure characterizing the whole group.

It will be found useful to express operations like this in condensed form ; it makes the operation easier to remember, and by adhering to the same symbols for identical quantities it helps to make the representation of the matter more consistent.

Let us call each observation X, and let N be the number of such observations. Let the operation of summing the observations be denoted by S, and let M_x stand for the *Average* of the X's, then $M_x = \dfrac{SX}{N}$.

The information given by the average, useful as it is, as regards the central tendency of the series, leaves us still in the dark about its tendency towards dispersion or spread. In order to complete our information about the distribution it is therefore desirable to have a single figure which expresses the scatter or spread, just as the arithmetic mean expresses its average or level. The most important measure of this kind is the *Standard Deviation*.

Before writing down its formula we must have some way of writing any deviation.

Using X and M_x in the same sense as before, let the difference between observation and average be denoted by x, thus

$$X \;-\; M_x = x$$
$$X' \;-\; M_x = x'$$
$$X'' \;-\; M_x = x''$$

The x's then represent the deviations of our X's from M_x. Summing all the X's we have

$$Sx = S(X - M_x) = SX - SM_x = SX - NM_x.$$

But
$$M_x = \frac{SX}{N} \; ; \;\; \therefore NM_x = SX$$

Hence,
$$Sx = SX - SX = 0.$$

This is one of the fundamental properties of the average : the algebraic sum of the deviation from it adds up to zero. This means that we cannot use the deviations as they are for measuring the dispersion. But the arithmetic mean has another very important property. If the deviations were taken from any other value of the scale the sum of their *squares* would always be greater than is the sum of the squared deviations from the mean. This property is now used for arriving at a measure of dispersion, the standard deviation.

It is simply the square root of the mean square deviation, just as the average is the mean of the measurements to the first power.

In symbols $\sigma_x = \sqrt{\dfrac{Sx^2}{N}}$.

It can, however, be more easily computed once we know the average M_x by the following formula

$$\sigma_x = \sqrt{\frac{SX^2}{N} - M_x{}^2},$$

which works with the observations X as they are, instead of with the deviations $X - M_x$.

If, for the sake of simplifying the arithmetic, the deviations of the observations are taken not from the true mean, M_x, but from an arbitrary value A (in this way we can avoid having to work with decimals), the formula for the mean then becomes

$$M_x = A_x + b, \text{ where } b = \frac{S(X - A_x)}{N}$$

according to the formula for the average in general.

The standard deviation becomes then

$$\sigma_x = \sqrt{\frac{S(X - A_x)^2}{N} - b^2}.$$

See also Fig. 5.7 and the calculation exhibited in paragraph 5.6 for *Grouped Distributions*.

APPENDIX III

Factors for Converting

(a) the Average Standard Deviation in Samples of n ($\bar{s}_n$)

(b) the Average Range in Samples of n ($\bar{w}_n$)

into the Population Standard Deviation (σ) according to the formulae

$$\sigma = \frac{\bar{s}_n}{b_n} \qquad \sigma = \frac{\bar{w}_n}{d_n}$$

n	b_n	d_n
2	0·564	1·128
3	0·724	1·693
4	0·798	2·059
5	0·841	2·326
6	0·869	2·534
7	0·888	2·704
8	0·903	2·847
9	0·914	2·970
10	0·923	3·078
11	0·930	3·173
12	0·936	3·258

(From Table II, Davies and Pearson, *Methods of Estimating from Samples the Population Standard Deviation*, J. R. St. S., vol. i, No. 1, 1934)

APPENDIX IV

Control Chart Limits for Averages

Factors by which to multiply

(a) The Average Standard Deviation in Samples of n ($\bar{s}_n$)

(b) The Average Range in Samples of n ($\bar{w}_n$)

in order to obtain the $\pm$ distances of the 1/40 and 1/1000 Limits respectivity from the Grand Average X.

The Factors were calculated according to the formulae :

1/40 Limits . .	$\dfrac{1\cdot96}{b_n\sqrt{n}}$	$\dfrac{1\cdot96}{d_n\sqrt{n}}$
1/1000 Limits . .	$\dfrac{3\cdot09}{b_n\sqrt{n}}$	$\dfrac{3\cdot09}{d_n\sqrt{n}}$

n	Inner limits $A_{0\cdot025}$	Outer limits $A_{0\cdot001}$	Inner limits $A'_{0\cdot025}$	Outer limits $A'_{0\cdot001}$
2	2·457	3·874	1·229	1·937
3	1·563	2·464	0·668	1·054
4	1·228	1·936	0·476	0·750
5	1·042	1·643	0·377	0·594
6	0·921	1·452	0·316	0·498
7	0·834	1·316	0·274	0·432
8	0·767	1·210	0·244	0·384
9	0·714	1·127	0·220	0·347
10	0·672	1·058	0·202	0·317
11	0·636	1·002	0·186	0·294
12	0·605	0·953	0·174	0·274

CONTROL CHART LIMITS FOR RANGES

Factors by which to multiply
(a) the Average Standard Deviation in Samples of n ($\bar{s}_n$)
(b) the Average Range in Samples of n ($\bar{w}_n$)

in order to obtain the Inner and Outer Control Limits for the Range in such Samples. These factors were calculated according to the formulae

	* Range at required Prob. Level as Multiple of σ b_n				Range at required Prob. Level as Multiple of d_n			
	LIMITS				LIMITS			
	Lower		Upper		Lower		Outer	
n	Inner $D_{.025}$	Outer $D_{.001}$	Inner $D_{.025}$	Outer $D_{.001}$	Inner $D'_{.025}$	Outer $D'_{.001}$	Inner $D'_{.025}$	Outer $D'_{.001}$
2	·071	·000	5·618	8·240	·036	·000	2·810	4·121
3	·415	·083	5·086	6·994	·177	·036	2·174	2·990
4	·739	·251	4·987	6·654	·287	·097	1·933	2·573
5	1·011	·440	4·995	6·517	·365	·159	1·806	2·356
6	1·220	·622	5·018	6·470	·418	·213	1·720	2·218
7	1·407	·777	5·055	6·452	·462	·255	1·660	2·120
8	1·562	·919	5·106	6·447	·495	·292	1·620	2·044
9	1·692	1·050	5·143	6·456	·522	·323	1·583	1·986
10	1·810	1·170	5·193	6·472	·543	·351	1·556	1·940
11	1·914	1·290	5·225	6·494	·651	·378	1·532	1·904
12	2·008	1·388	5·255	6·505	·577	·399	1·510	1·870

It should be noted that the Factors A and D in the above Tables are multipliers for the Average Standard Deviation in Samples of n ($\bar{s}_n$), whereas the A and D factors of Table 10 and 13 of British Standard Institution, 600 R : 1942 are multipliers for the Population Standard Deviation (σ).

The values given for the Factors " D' " differ slightly from those in Table 13A British Standard Institution, 600 R : 1942. They had to be recalculated as those given in 600 R are slightly in error.

* . . . The numerator in the formula is taken from Pearson and Hartley, " The Prob. Integral of the Range . . .," *Biometrika*, vol. xxxii, 1942

APPENDIX V

Probability Curves Showing Poisson's Exponential Summation

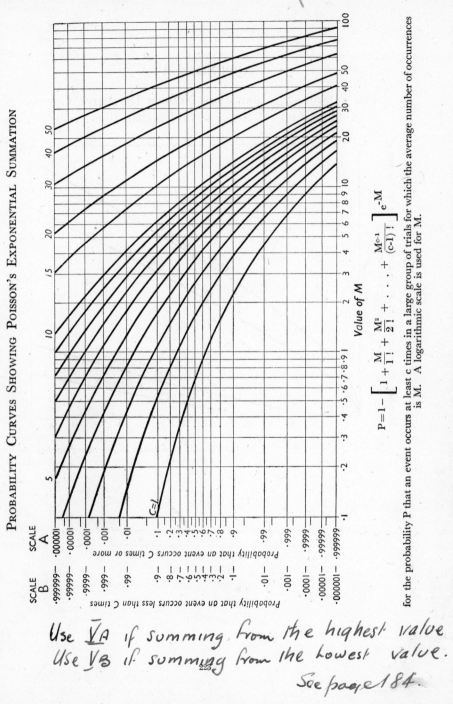

$$P = 1 - \left[1 + \frac{M}{1!} + \frac{M^2}{2!} + \ldots + \frac{M^{c-1}}{(c-1)!} \right] e^{-M}$$

for the probability P that an event occurs at least c times in a large group of trials for which the average number of occurrences is M. A logarithmic scale is used for M.

Use VA if summing from the highest value
Use VB if summing from the lowest value.

See page 184.

APPENDIX VI

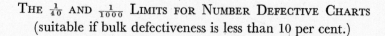

The $\frac{1}{40}$ and $\frac{1}{1000}$ Limits for Number Defective Charts
(suitable if bulk defectiveness is less than 10 per cent.)

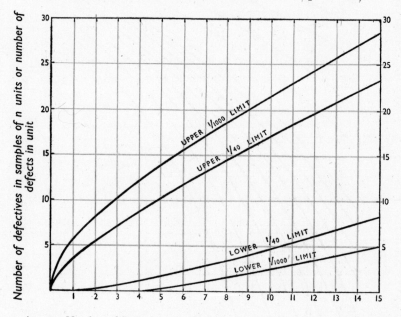

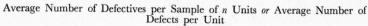

Average Number of Defectives per Sample of *n* Units *or* Average Number of
Defects per Unit

APPENDIX VII

The three charts of this Appendix are after L. E. Simon,
An Engineer's Manual of Statistical Method (1941)

Chart $0.5 = I_Q$

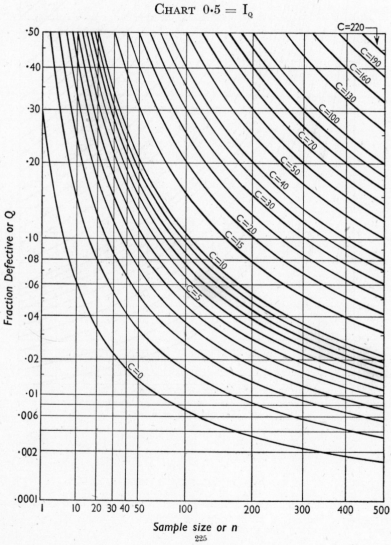

Fraction Defective or Q

Sample size or n

CHART $0.9 = I_Q$

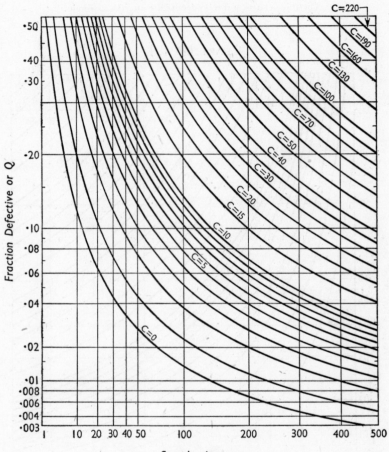

Sample size or n

CHART $0 \cdot 1 = I_Q$

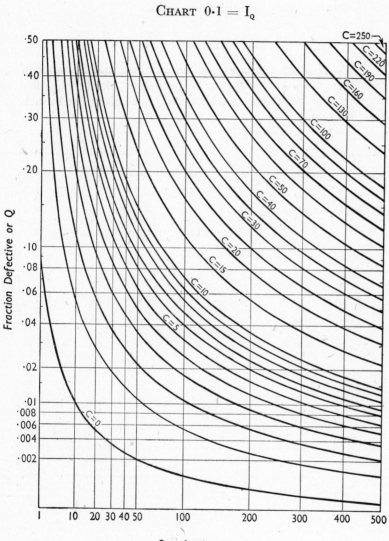

Fraction Defective or Q

Sample size or n

APPENDIX VIII

TABLE 1

For a given combination of Sample Size and Number of Defectives, read with 50 per cent. probability the Lot Quality as percentage defectiveness which could have given rise to such Sample Quality :—

No. of Defectives \ Sample size	50	100	200	300	400	500
0	1·4	·7	·35	·23	·18	·14
1	3·3	1·7	·84	·56	·42	·33
2	5·2	2·7	1·3	·9	·67	·53
3	7·3	3·6	1·8	1·2	·90	·73
4	9·0	4·6	2·3	1·6	1·2	·93
5	11·0	5·7	2·8	1·9	1·4	1·1
6	13·0	6·7	3·3	2·2	1·7	1·3
7	15·0	7·6	3·8	2·6	1·9	1·5
8	16·8	8·6	4·3	2·8	2·2	1·7
9	19·0	9·6	4·8	3·0	2·4	1·9
10	21·0	10·5	5·3	3·5	2·7	2·1

TABLE 2

For a given combination of Sample Size and Number of Defectives, read with 80 per cent. probability the Lot Quality as percentage defectiveness which could have given rise to such a Sample Quality:—

No. of Defectives \ Sample size	50	100	200	300	400	500
0	·2– 4·5	·1 – 2·3	·05–1·2	·035– ·78	·029– ·58	·011– ·46
1	1·8– 7·6	·5 – 3·8	·26–2·0	·17–1·3	·14–1·0	·10– ·78
2	2·2–10·2	1·1 – 5·2	·55–2·6	·38–1·7	·28–1·3	·22–1·1
3	3·5–12·9	1·8 – 6·5	·88–3·3	·54–2·2	·45–1·7	·36–1·3
4	5·0–15·3	2·5 – 7·8	1·2 –4·0	·80–2·7	·63–2·0	·50–1·6
5	6·4–18·0	3·1 – 9·0	1·58–4·6	1·05–3·1	·80–2·3	·63–1·8
6	8·0–20·0	4·0 –10·3	1·95–5·3	1·3 –3·5	1·0 –2·6	·78–2·1
7	9·5–22·0	4·7 –11·5	2·35–5·7	1·55–3·9	1·2 –2·9	·93–2·3
8	11·0–24·6	5·5 –12·6	2·7 –6·4	1·8 –4·3	1·4 –3·2	1·1 –2·6
9	12·9–27·0	6·4 –14·0	3·1 –7·0	2·1 –4·7	1·6 –3·5	1·3 –2·8
10	14·4–29·0	7·1 –15·0	3·6 –7·6	2·35–5·0	1·8 –3·8	1·4 –3·1

TABLE 3

For a given combination of Sample Size and Lot Quality in percentage defectiveness, read with 80 per cent. Probability the Range of the Number of Defectives such Samples might be expected to contain :—

Lot quality \ Sample size	50	100	200	300	400	500
·5	0–1	0– 1	0– 2	0– 3	1– 3	1– 4
1·0	0–1	0– 2	1– 3	1– 5	2– 6	3– 7
2·0	0–2	1– 3	2– 6	3– 9	5–11	6–14
3·0	0–3	1– 5	3– 9	6–12	8–16	10–19
4·0	1–3	2– 6	5–11	8–16	11–21	15–25
5·0	1–4	3– 7	7–14	11–20	15–25	19–30
6·0	2–5	4– 9	8–16	13–23	18–30	23–36
7·0	2–6	4–10	10–18	16–26	22–34	28–42
8·0	2–6	5–11	12–20	18–30	25–38	33–47
9·0	3–7	6–12	13–23	21–30	29–43	37–53
10·0	3–7	7–13	15–25	24–36	34–47	42–58

APPENDIX IXa

SPECIMEN OF DODGE-ROMIG TABLES FOR SINGLE SAMPLING

TABLE SL-10 Lot Tolerance per cent. Defective = 10·0 %

Process Average %	·0–10			·11–1·00			1·01–2·00			2·01–3·00			3·01–4·00			4·01–5·00		
Lot size	n	c	AOQL %	n	c	AOQL %	n	c	AOQL %	n	c	AOQL %	n	c	AOQL %	n	c	AOQL %
1–20	All	0	0	All	0	0	All	0	0	All	0	0	All	0	0	All	0	0
21–50	17	0	1·3	17	0	1·3	17	0	1·3	17	0	1·3	17	0	1·3	17	0	1·3
51–100	20	0	1·5	20	0	1·5	20	0	1·5	33	1	1·7	33	1	1·7	33	1	1·7
101–200	22	0	1·5	22	0	1·5	35	1	2·0	45	2	2·2	48	2	2·2	60	3	2·4
201–300	23	0	1·5	38	1	1·9	50	2	2·3	65	3	2·4	75	4	2·6	85	5	2·7
301–400	23	0	1·5	38	1	1·5	50	2	2·4	65	3	2·5	90	5	2·7	100	6	2·9
401–500	23	0	1·5	38	1	2·0	50	2	2·5	75	4	2·8	90	5	2·9	110	7	3·2
501–600	23	0	1·5	38	1	2·1	65	3	2·7	80	4	3·0	100	6	3·2	125	8	3·3
601–800	23	0	1·6	38	1	2·1	65	3	2·8	90	5	3·1	100	6	3·3	140	9	3·4
801–1,000	39	1	2·1	50	2	2·6	65	3	2·8	90	5	3·2	115	7	3·4	150	10	3·7
1,001–2,000	39	1	2·1	50	2	2·6	80	4	3·1	105	6	3·4	140	9	3·9	195	14	4·4
2,001–3,000	39	1	2·1	50	2	2·6	80	4	3·1	115	7	3·7	165	11	4·1	230	17	4·7
3,001–4,000	39	1	2·1	50	2	2·6	90	5	3·4	130	8	3·8	190	13	4·4	255	19	4·8
4,001–5,000	39	1	2·1	50	2	2·5	90	5	3·5	130	8	3·9	200	14	4·5	270	20	4·9
5,001–7,000	39	1	2·1	65	3	3·0	105	6	3·6	140	9	4·1	200	14	4·6	295	22	5·0
7,001–10,000	39	1	2·2	65	3	3·0	105	6	3·6	150	10	4·2	210	15	4·7	315	24	5·2
10,001–20,000	39	1	2·2	65	3	3·0	120	7	3·7	150	10	4·3	240	17	4·8	340	26	5·4
20,001–50,000	39	1	2·2	80	4	3·2	120	7	3·7	165	11	4·4	260	19	5·0	380	30	5·7
50,000–100,000	39	1	2·2	95	5	3·3	130	8	4·0	180	12	4·4	270	20	5·1	380	30	5·7

n = Size of Sample ; entry of " All " indicates that each piece in lot is to be inspected
c = Allowable Defect Number for Sample   AOQL = Average Outgoing Quality Limit

APPENDIX IXb

SPECIMEN OF DODGE-ROMIG TABLES FOR DOUBLE SAMPLING

TABLE DL-10 Lot Tolerance per cent. Defective = 10·0 %

Lot size	0-10 · n₁	c₂	n₂	n₁+n₂	c₂	AOQL in %	·11-1·00 · n₁	c₁	n₂	n₁+n₂	c₂	AOQL in %	1·01-2·00 · n₁	c₁	n₂	n₁+n₂	c₂	AOQL in %
1-20	All	0	—	—	—	0	All	0	—	—	—	0	All	0	—	—	—	0
21-50	17	0	—	—	—	1·3	17	0	—	—	—	1·3	17	0	—	—	0	1·3
51-100	25	0	13	38	1	1·6	25	0	13	38	1	1·6	25	0	13	38	1	1·6
101-200	27	0	15	42	1	1·8	27	0	15	42	1	1·8	27	0	28	55	2	2·1
201-300	27	0	16	43	1	1·9	27	0	30	57	2	2·2	27	0	43	70	3	2·4
301-400	27	0	17	44	1	1·9	27	0	33	60	2	2·2	27	0	43	70	3	2·5
401-500	28	0	16	44	1	1·9	28	0	32	60	2	2·3	28	0	57	85	4	2·7
501-600	28	0	17	45	1	1·9	28	0	32	60	2	2·3	28	0	57	85	4	2·8
601-800	28	0	17	45	1	2·0	28	0	47	75	3	2·6	28	0	57	85	4	2·9
801-1,000	28	0	32	60	2	2·3	28	0	47	75	3	2·6	28	0	72	100	5	3·0
1,001-2,000	28	0	32	60	2	2·4	28	0	47	75	3	2·7	45	1	70	115	6	3·3
2,001-3,000	28	0	32	60	2	2·4	28	0	47	75	3	2·7	45	1	85	130	7	3·5
3,001-4,000	28	0	32	60	2	2·4	28	0	62	90	4	2·9	45	1	85	130	7	3·5
4,001-5,000	28	0	32	60	2	2·4	28	0	62	90	4	3·0	45	1	95	140	8	3·7
5,001-7,000	28	0	32	60	2	2·4	28	0	62	90	4	3·0	45	1	95	140	8	3·8
7,001-10,000	28	0	32	60	2	2·5	28	0	62	90	4	3·0	45	1	95	140	8	3·8
10,001-20,000	28	0	32	60	2	2·5	28	0	62	90	4	3·0	45	1	110	155	9	3·9
20,001-50,000	28	0	32	60	2	2·5	28	0	72	100	5	3·3	45	1	120	165	10	3·9
50,000-100,000	28	0	32	60	2	2·5	28	0	72	100	5	3·3	45	1	135	180	11	4·2

n_1 = Size of First Sample; n_2 = Size of Second Sample; entry of " All " indicates that each piece in lot is to be inspected

Lot size	2·01-3·00						3·01-4·00						4·01-5·00					
Process Average %	Trial 1		Trial 2			AOQL in %	Trial 1		Trial 2			AOQL in %	Trial 1		Trial 2			AOQL in %
	n_1	c_1	n_2	n_1+n_2	c_2		n_1	c_1	n_2	n_1+n_2	c_2		n_1	c_1	n_2	n_1+n_2	c_2	
1-20	All	0	—	—	—	0	All	0	—	—	—	0	All	0	—	—	—	0
21-50	17	0	—	—	—	1·3	17	0	—	—	—	1·3	17	0	—	—	—	1·3
51-100	25	0	24	49	2	1·8	25	0	24	49	2	1·8	25	0	24	49	2	1·8
101-200	27	0	38	65	3	2·3	27	0	53	80	4	2·4	27	0	53	80	4	2·4
201-300	27	0	53	80	4	2·7	43	1	62	105	6	2·8	43	1	82	125	8	3·0
301-400	44	1	66	110	6	2·9	44	1	86	130	8	3·1	60	2	90	150	10	3·2
401-500	44	1	76	120	7	3·1	44	1	101	145	9	3·3	60	2	105	165	11	3·4
501-600	45	1	75	120	7	3·3	60	2	100	160	10	3·4	75	3	115	190	13	3·6
601-800	45	1	90	135	8	3·5	60	2	110	170	11	3·7	75	3	140	215	15	3·9
801-1,000	45	1	90	135	8	3·5	60	2	125	185	12	3·9	90	4	150	240	17	4·1
1,001-2,000	60	2	105	165	10	3·9	75	3	150	225	15	4·3	115	6	200	315	23	4·8
2,000-3,000	60	2	130	190	12	4·1	75	3	175	250	17	4·4	130	7	235	365	27	5·0
3,001-4,000	60	2	130	190	12	4·2	90	4	170	260	18	4·6	130	7	255	385	29	5·1
4,001-5,000	60	2	140	200	13	4·3	90	4	180	270	19	4·7	140	8	270	410	31	5·2
5,001-7,000	60	2	140	200	13	4·4	90	4	205	295	21	4·9	140	8	315	455	35	5·3
7,001-10,000	60	2	155	215	14	4·4	90	4	220	310	22	5·0	140	8	340	480	37	5·4
10,001-20,000	60	2	165	225	15	4·4	100	5	230	330	24	5·1	155	9	370	525	41	5·6
20,001-50,000	75	3	165	240	16	4·5	100	5	280	380	28	5·2	163	10	405	570	45	5·9
50,000-100,000	75	3	200	275	19	4·8	115	6	285	400	30	5·3	165	10	440	605	48	6·2

c_1 = Allowable Defect Number for First Sample ; c_2 = Allowable Defect Number for First and Second Samples Combined

AOQL = Average Outgoing Quality Limit

APPENDIX IXc

DODGE-ROMIG, SINGLE SAMPLING LOT INSPECTION TABLE—BASED ON STATED VALUES OF AVERAGE OUTGOING QUALITY LIMIT (CONDENSED)

The body of this table gives such co-ordinated pairs of sample size, n, and allowable number of defectives, c, as will enable one to meet the stipulation that the defectiveness in the outgoing total shall not exceed a stated amount.

	Average Outgoing Quality Limit																			
Lot Size	·5%				1·0%				2·0%				5·0%				10·0%			
Process Average %	·5% > $\bar{p}$ ≥ ·5%				1% > $\bar{p}$ ≥ ·1%				2% > $\bar{p}$ ≥ 2%				5% > $\bar{p}$ ≥ 5%				10% > $\bar{p}$ ≥ 10%			
	n	c	n	c	n	c	n	c	n	c	n	c	n	c	n	c	n	c	n	c
100–200	55	0	55	0	32	0	32	0	35	1	35	1	16	1	24	2	13	2	18	3
201–300	60	0	60	0	33	0	65	1	37	1	37	1	25	2	25	2	18	3	23	4
301–400	60	0	60	0	70	1	70	1	38	1	60	2	26	2	35	3	24	4	29	5
401–500	65	0	125	1	70	1	70	1	60	2	60	2	36	3	46	4	24	4	30	5
501–600	130	1	130	1	75	1	75	1	60	2	60	2	37	3	47	4	24	4	36	6
601–700	140	1	140	1	75	1	120	2	65	2	85	3	48	4	60	5	31	5	42	7
801–1,000	145	1	145	1	120	2	120	2	65	2	90	3	48	4	70	6	37	6	49	8
1,001–2,000	155	1	240	2	130	2	180	3	95	3	120	4	60	5	85	7	44	7	65	10
2,001–3,000	250	2	250	2	185	3	235	4	120	4	180	6	75	6	125	10	50	8	85	13
3,001–4,000	255	2	355	3	185	3	295	5	155	5	210	7	85	7	140	11	65	10	100	15
4,001–5,000	360	3	460	4	245	4	300	5	155	5	245	8	100	8	155	12	65	10	120	18
5,001–7,000	370	3	475	4	305	5	420	7	185	6	280	9	115	9	185	14	80	12	135	20
7,001–10,000	485	4	595	5	310	5	430	7	220	7	350	11	130	10	225	17	85	13	160	23
10,001–20,000	615	5	855	7	435	7	635	10	290	9	460	14	170	13	305	22	110	16	190	27
20,001–50,000	875	7	1,410	11	575	9	990	15	395	12	720	21	215	16	400	28	130	19	225	31
50,001–100,000	1,290	10	2,130	16	790	12	1,520	22	505	15	955	27	275	20	450	31	155	22	260	35

APPENDIX X

VALUES OF THE VARIANCE RATIO (F) AT THE 5 PER CENT.
(in black type), 1 PER CENT. (in roman type), 0·1 PER
CENT. (in *italics*), LEVEL OF THE F-DISTRIBUTION.

n_1 Degrees of Freedom for Greater Mean Square

n_2	2	3	4	5	6	8	12	24	∞
2	**19·0**	**19·2**	**19·3**	**19·3**	**19·3**	**19·4**	**19·4**	**19·5**	**19·5**
	99·0	99·2	99·3	99·3	99·3	99·4	99·4	99·5	99·5
	999·0	*999·2*	*999·2*	*999·2*	*999·2*	*999·4*	*999·4*	*999·4*	*999·4*
3	**9·6**	**9·3**	**9·1**	**9·0**	**8·9**	**8·8**	**8·7**	**8·6**	**8·5**
	30·8	29·5	28·7	28·2	27·9	27·5	27·1	26·6	26·1
	148·5	*141·1*	*137·1*	*134·6*	*132·8*	*130·6*	*128·3*	*125·9*	*123·5*
4	**7·0**	**6·6**	**6·4**	**6·3**	**6·2**	**6·0**	**5·9**	**5·8**	**5·6**
	18·0	16·7	16·0	15·5	15·2	14·8	14·4	13·9	13·5
	61·2	*56·2*	*53·4*	*51·7*	*50·5*	*49·0*	*47·4*	*45·8*	*44·1*
5	**5·8**	**5·4**	**5·2**	**5·1**	**5·0**	**4·8**	**4·7**	**4·5**	**4·4**
	13·3	12·1	11·4	11·0	10·7	10·3	9·9	9·5	9·0
	36·6	*33·2*	*31·1*	*29·8*	*28·8*	*27·6*	*26·4*	*25·1*	*23·8*
6	**5·1**	**4·8**	**4·5**	**4·4**	**4·3**	**4·2**	**4·0**	**3·8**	**3·7**
	10·9	9·8	9·2	8·8	8·5	8·1	7·7	7·3	6·9
	27·0	*23·7*	*21·9*	*20·8*	*20·0*	*19·0*	*18·0*	*17·0*	*15·8*
7	**4·7**	**4·4**	**4·1**	**4·0**	**3·9**	**3·7**	**3·6**	**3·4**	**3·2**
	9·6	8·5	7·9	7·5	7·2	6·8	6·5	6·1	5·7
	21·7	*18·8*	*17·2*	*16·2*	*15·5*	*14·6*	*13·7*	*12·7*	*11·7*
8	**4·5**	**4·1**	**3·8**	**3·7**	**3·6**	**3·4**	**3·3**	**3·1**	**2·9**
	8·7	7·6	7·0	6·6	6·4	6·0	5·7	5·3	4·9
	18·5	*15·8*	*14·4*	*13·5*	*12·9*	*12·0*	*11·2*	*10·3*	*9·3*
9	**4·3**	**3·9**	**3·6**	**3·5**	**3·4**	**3·2**	**3·1**	**2·9**	**2·7**
	8·0	7·0	6·4	6·1	5·8	5·5	5·1	4·7	4·3
	16·4	*13·9*	*12·6*	*11·7*	*11·1*	*10·4*	*9·6*	*8·7*	*7·8*
10	**4·1**	**3·7**	**3·5**	**3·3**	**3·2**	**3·1**	**2·9**	**2·7**	**2·5**
	7·6	6·6	6·0	5·6	5·4	5·1	4·7	4·3	3·9
	14·9	*12·6*	*11·3*	*10·5*	*9·9*	*9·2*	*8·5*	*7·6*	*6·8*

n_1 Degrees of Freedom for Greater Mean Square

n_2	2	3	4	5	6	8	12	24	∞
12	3·9	3·5	3·3	3·1	3·0	2·9	2·7	2·5	2·3
	6·9	6·0	5·4	5·1	4·8	4·5	4·2	3·8	3·4
	13·0	*10·8*	*9·6*	*8·9*	*8·4*	*7·7*	*7·0*	*6·3*	*5·4*
14	3·7	3·3	3·1	3·0	2·9	2·7	2·5	2·4	2·1
	6·5	5·6	5·0	4·7	4·5	4·1	3·8	3·4	3·0
	11·8	*9·7*	*8·6*	*7·9*	*7·4*	*6·8*	*6·1*	*5·4*	*4·6*
16	3·6	3·2	3·0	2·9	2·7	2·6	2·4	2·2	2·0
	6·2	5·3	4·8	4·4	4·2	3·9	3·6	3·2	2·8
	11·0	*9·0*	*7·9*	*7·3*	*6·8*	*6·2*	*5·6*	*4·9*	*4·1*
18	3·6	3·2	2·9	2·8	2·7	2·5	2·3	2·2	1·9
	6·0	5·1	4·6	4·3	4·0	3·7	3·4	3·0	2·6
	10·4	*8·5*	*7·5*	*6·8*	*6·4*	*5·8*	*5·1*	*4·5*	*3·7*
20	3·5	3·1	2·9	2·7	2·6	2·5	2·3	2·1	1·8
	5·9	4·9	4·4	4·1	3·9	3·6	3·2	2·9	2·4
	10·0	*8·1*	*7·1*	*6·5*	*6·0*	*5·4*	*4·8*	*4·2*	*3·4*
25	3·4	3·0	2·8	2·6	2·5	2·3	2·2	2·0	1·7
	5·6	4·7	4·2	3·9	3·6	3·3	3·0	2·6	2·2
	9·2	*7·5*	*6·5*	*5·9*	*5·5*	*4·9*	*4·3*	*3·7*	*2·9*
30	3·3	2·9	2·7	2·5	2·4	2·3	2·1	1·9	1·6
	5·4	4·5	4·0	3·7	3·5	3·2	2·8	2·5	2·0
	8·8	*7·1*	*6·1*	*5·5*	*5·1*	*4·6*	*4·0*	*3·4*	*2·6*
60	3·2	2·8	2·5	2·4	2·3	2·1	1·9	1·7	1·4
	5·0	4·1	3·7	3·3	3·1	2·8	2·5	2·1	1·6
	7·8	*6·2*	*5·3*	*4·8*	*4·4*	*3·9*	*3·3*	*2·7*	*1·9*
∞	3·0	2·6	2·4	2·2	2·1	1·9	1·8	1·5	1·0
	4·6	3·8	3·3	3·0	2·8	2·5	2·2	1·8	1·0
	6·9	*5·4*	*4·6*	*4·1*	*3·7*	*3·3*	*2·7*	*2·1*	*1·0*

(This table is a condensed version of Appendix C2, Croxton and Cowder, *Applied General Statistics*, London, Pitman & Sons, Ltd.)

APPENDIX XI

This is intended to be a brief summary of instructions for the proper use of the important tests for identity of population if two or more samples are available.

The question is always whether the differences which we observe between the means or standard deviations in the samples are compatible with the assumption that such differences could arise by mere fluctuations of chance in samples coming from one and the same parent distribution. The answer is in the affirmative if the observed difference could arise by mere chance at least 5 times in 100, in the negative if it could arise less than 5 times in 100.

The method consists in expressing the observed difference by the standard deviation in the sampling distribution, i.e. in the distribution of the statistical constant in question. The greater that ratio, the greater is the likelihood that the samples come from different distributions or that the difference is " real."

I

A—SIGNIFICANCE OF DIFFERENCE BETWEEN TWO MEANS
(It is assumed that the Parent distribution is normal, or nearly so.)

(1) *For large N*

We form the ratio $\dfrac{\text{Difference between Means}}{\text{Standard Deviation of Means}}$, in symbols $t = \dfrac{\bar{x}_1 - \bar{x}_2}{\sigma_p/\sqrt{N}}$, where σ_p is the standard deviation in the population of individuals and N the sample size. As a sufficiently close estimate of σ_p, we use the standard deviation in the samples (s). In general, i.e. for samples of different s and n, we have, remembering that the variance of a compound distribution equals the sum of the partial variances,

$$t = \frac{\bar{x}_1 - \bar{x}_2}{\sqrt{\dfrac{s_1^2}{N_1} + \dfrac{s_2^2}{N_2}}}, \text{ which formula reduces to } t = \frac{\bar{x}_1 - \bar{x}_2}{s\sqrt{\dfrac{2}{N}}}$$

if the samples have sensibly the same s and the same N.

If now the quantity t exceeds 2 or 3, this means that a difference as observed, either in the positive or negative direction, could arise by mere chance less than 1 in 20, or 1 in

370 times, respectively. As 1/20 already represents 5 per cent., we consider such differences to be significant, that is, as pointing to a " real " difference between the samples.

The connection between the multiple of $\sigma_p/\sqrt{N}$ and the probability level is derived from the table of the Probability Integral or the Error Function (Appendix I).

(2) *For small N.*

The principle of the test is the same as before, but we cannot use the Error Function in this case for the following reason.

The quantity $\dfrac{\bar{x}_1 - \bar{x}_2}{\sigma_p/\sqrt{N}}$ is distributed normally if the parent distribution is normal, and the Error Function applies therefore for the connection of a given multiple of $\dfrac{\sigma_p}{\sqrt{N}}$ with a level of probability. In large samples it is permitted, as observed above, to regard the standard deviation in the sample, s, as a sufficiently close estimate of the standard deviation in the population σ_p, and we can therefore rely on the probabilities as given by the Error Function for certain multiples of $\dfrac{s}{\sqrt{N}}$. In small samples, however, the standard deviation differs from that of the population, and this the more the smaller the sample. The quantity $t = \dfrac{\bar{x}_1 - \bar{x}_2}{s/\sqrt{N}}$ is no longer distributed normally.

This means that certain multiples of $\dfrac{s}{\sqrt{N}}$ are now connected with probability levels different from those we found to correspond to such multiples in the Error Function.

For testing the difference of means in small samples, therefore, we must use tables of a different function, called " Student's t function " (after Student, the pen-name of its discoverer), of which a condensed version is given below.

The quantity t is obtained according to the formula

$$t = \bar{x}_1 - \bar{x}_2 \sqrt{\frac{N_1 N_2 (N_1 + N_2 - 2)}{(N_1 + N_2) (\Sigma x_1^2 + \Sigma x_2^2)}}$$

where x_1, x_2 are the deviations from $\bar{x}_1$, $\bar{x}_2$ respectively.

TABLE OF "STUDENT'S t"

The values in the body of the table represent such multiples of the Standard Error on both sides of the Mean as are required for accommodating specified percentages of t, viz. 50 per cent., 90 per cent., 95 per cent., and 99 per cent. for a given number (n) of Degrees of Freedom. The percentages P, of t occurring beyond these values are 50 per cent., 10 per cent., 5 per cent., and 1 per cent. respectively, and the table is so arranged as to refer to there percentages.

TABLE OF "STUDENT'S t"

P / n	·50	·10	·05	·01
1	1·000	6·34	12·71	63·66
2	·816	2·92	4·30	9·92
3	·765	2·35	3·18	5·84
4	·741	2·13	2·78	4·60
5	·727	2·02	2·57	4·03
6	·718	1·94	2·45	3·71
7	·711	1·90	2·36	3·50
8	·706	1·86	2·31	3·36
9	·703	1·83	2·26	3·25
10	·700	1·81	2·23	3·17
11–15	·697–·691	1·80–1·75	2·20–2·13	3·11–2·95
16–20	·690–·687	1·75–1·72	2·12–2·09	2·92–2·84
21–30	·686–·683	1·72–1·70	2·08–2·04	2·83–2·75
31–100	·682–·677	1·69–1·66	2·03–1·98	2·72–2·63
101–1000	·677–·674	1·66–1·65	1·98–1·96	2·63–2·58
∞	·674	1·64	1·96	2·58

The table is entered with $n = N - 1$ on the vertical scale if the samples are of the same size, and with $n = N_1 + N_2 - 2$ if they are of different size. Our observed value of t is then compared at this level with the values in the body of the table, and the probability with which to expect a difference like ours on mere chance is then read on the horizontal scale. If for a given n, the observed t is greater than the corresponding value in column P = ·05, this means that such a value of t has a probability of less than 5 per cent. in samples coming from one and the same lot, and we consider it to signify different populations.

B—Significance of Difference Between Two Standard Deviations

(1) *For large samples* *

We form the quantity $\frac{\sigma_p}{\sqrt{2N}}$ which is the standard deviation in the distribution of standard deviations of samples of N, and proceeding as before—that is, according to whether the observed difference between two standard deviations exceeds two or three times the quantity $\frac{\sigma_p}{\sqrt{2N}}$ we conclude, on the basis of the Error Function, that such differences could occur less than 1 in 20 or 1 in 370 times. If so, we regard the difference as pointing to a real difference between the two samples ; otherwise, their variability is assumed to be essentially the same. As a sufficiently close estimate of σ_p we use again the observed standard deviation.

(2) *For small samples and large samples in non-normal distributions*

We form the ratio of the squares of the observed standard deviations $\frac{s_1^2}{s_2^2}$, and use the tables of the Ratio Variance (based upon the Beta-Function, Appendix X) for ascertaining how often such a ratio is likely to arise if both samples have come from the same population. As the fundamental level of probability serving as the border-line between " apparent " and " real " differences, we again take the 5 per cent. level (see Chapter IV, paragraph 4.3, 4.5).

II

C—Testing the Significance of Difference Between More than Two Means

We form the quantity

$$\frac{n \text{ (Variance between Sample Means)}}{\text{Average Variance within Samples of } n}$$

which is familiar from Chapter IV. In symbols $\frac{n\text{Var}_1}{\text{Var}_2}$.

We now test $\frac{n\text{Var}_1}{\text{Var}_2}$ *as if* $n\text{Var}_1$ was the variance of a second

* Normality of Parent distribution assumed

sample differing in size from those from which Var_2 was obtained. That is, we use exactly the same kind of test as was considered in B (2) where the standard deviations were compared for their own sake.

The explanation for this procedure is given in Chapter IV, dealing with the analysis of variance method.

D—SIGNIFICANCE OF DIFFERENCE BETWEEN MORE THAN TWO STANDARD DEVIATIONS

Denoting the variances by V_1, V_2, V_3, V_4 . . ., we form the quantity

$$\frac{\text{Geometric Mean of Variances}}{\text{Arithmetic Mean of Variances}}$$

in symbols

$$L = \frac{n \cdot \sqrt[n]{V_1 \cdot V_2 \cdot V_3 \cdot V_4 \ldots V_n \cdot}}{V_1 + V_2 + V_3 + V_4 + \ldots + V_n}.$$

One property of L is that it decreases in value as the variances differ more among themselves. It has a maximum value of 1 if the variances are equal. The 5 per cent. probability level of significance for various combinations of degrees of freedom, that is, for different numbers of variances (n) and different sample sizes (N) can be read from tables. If the value of L sinks below that level we conclude that the differences between the variances are real.

(This test is due to E. S. Pearson and Neyman, 1931, and is in this form applicable if the number of specimens, N, is the same in all samples.)

III

E—SIGNIFICANCE OF DIFFERENCE BETWEEN FREQUENCIES

If both mean and standard deviation are sensibly equal, the question of whether both samples have come from the same population still depends on whether the same type of Law of Chance governs the distribution in both samples and in the population. The criterion for this most important question lies in the corresponding *class frequencies*. If these do not differ significantly for given values of the variable from one sample to the other, and between samples and population, and if mean and standard deviation are sensibly the same, then we can be satisfied that the samples have come from one population.

For testing the significance of differences between the corresponding class frequencies in two distributions whose mean and standard deviation are sensibly the same, the χ^2 -test is applied, of which the barest outline has been given in paragraph 3.5.

IV

F—Significance of Difference Between Fraction or Percentage Defectiveness

(a) *Comparing two sampling results*

If two samples of sizes n_1 and n_2 show m_1 and m_2 defectives respectively, the difference of sample qualities, $\frac{m_1}{n_1} - \frac{m_2}{n_2}$, is tested for significance by the

$$\text{Standard Error} = \sqrt{\frac{n_2{}^3 m_1(n_1 - m_1) + n^3{}_1 m_2(n_2 - m_2)}{n_1{}^3 n_2{}^3}},$$

which for samples of equal size, $n_1 = n_2 = n$, reduces to

$$\text{Standard Error} = \sqrt{\frac{m_1(n - m_1) + m_2(n - m_2)}{n^3}}.$$

If the difference $\frac{m_1}{n_1} - \frac{m_2}{n_2}$, or for equal sample size $\frac{m_1}{n} - \frac{m_2}{n}$, exceeds twice the standard error, this is taken as denoting that the samples represent different populations.

(b) *Comparing more than two sampling results*

We calculate the mean defectiveness q, for all the samples drawn from different lots, and form the standard deviation for a homogenous population as $\sigma' = \sqrt{\frac{pq}{n}}$, where $p + q = 1$ and n is the total number of specimens (see para. 6.5). We now calculate the standard deviation of the deviations, x_i, of our sample qualities expressed as fractions from the mean defectiveness, q, according to the formula $\sigma'' = \sqrt{\frac{\Sigma(x)^2}{n-1}}$.

The quantity $Q = \frac{\sigma''}{\sigma'}$ then affords a measure of the homogeneity, or otherwise, of the population. The more it deviates from unity, the less likely is it that the probability of a defective is the same for all the lots from which the samples were drawn.

APPENDIX XII

METHODS OF CONDENSING THE INFORMATION DERIVABLE FROM CONTROL CHARTS

(1) There are various methods for condensing the information contained in the quality control charts so as to give, on one hand, the higher management a concise idea of the quality of the work over a certain period, and, on the other hand, to stimulate production in the shops by exhibiting the quality of the product.

One of these methods consists in providing the higher management with a weekly summary containing all the necessary information about the week's work as far as the operations are under quality control supervision.

The management can read in those forms the extent to which the control chart technique was employed in a given production branch, the number of charts, number of persons employed, number of samples within and without control limits—and thus the state of statistical control—the number of samples within and without specifications—and thus the state of economic control. The quality control foreman, on the other hand, by summarizing the week's inspection results in this way, is in a position to inform the shop people reliably on the quality of their product, and so to give them an idea to what extent their work comes up to specifications.

(2) It is, however, feasible to condense still further the information based upon, say, a week's experience by using a *Quality Index*—that is, a single figure—indicating the quality of the product.* Needless to say that a single figure like that can be arrived at only by sacrificing a great amount of useful information, but it has, on the other hand, the advantage of facilitating comparisons between different weeks. Whether the loss of information is outweighed by the increase in conciseness is a question which the higher management and the shop management must decide for themselves, and the preference for one or the other method will be very often a matter of taste.

The principles underlying the construction of such an index are these. From the specifications it is easy to arrive at control limits for 100 per cent. perfect product (see paragraph 2.6).

---

* The conception of the Quality Index is due to Mr. B. Taylor and Mr. R. F. H. Banister. The mathematical structure given here differs, however, considerably from the one used by Messrs. Taylor and Banister.

It is then possible to draw control limits at such distances from the specification mean as would result from say, 5 per cent., 10 per cent., 15 per cent. defective product. For this purpose we again make use of the properties of normal distributions to which, we can assume, our distributions of sample means will satisfactorily approximate.

For 100 per cent. perfect product, that is, for product of which practically nothing exceeds specifications, the distance specification mean-tolerance (be it upper or lower) corresponds to 3σ approximately, and the distance specification mean—1/1000 limit to $\frac{3\sigma}{\sqrt{n}}$ or, denoting the standard deviation of the means $\frac{\sigma}{\sqrt{n}}$ by σ', to $3\sigma'$.

If now, 5 per cent., say, of the product exceeds specifications, the range, and, therefore, the standard deviation in both, parent distribution of individuals and sampling distribution of means, increases. Let us denote these new standard deviations by σ_1 and σ_1' respectively. It is evident that the distance specification mean-tolerance will now be less than $3\sigma_1$, and the distance between the specification mean and former control limit less than $3\sigma_1'$. What we are now interested in is what fraction of $3\sigma_1'$ corresponds to the control limit distance for perfect product. Knowing that fraction, we can easily obtain σ_1', and from it the new control lines for 5 per cent. defective product.

For obtaining the answer to our problem we consult the tables of the Probability Integral, Appendix I. According to our stipulation, 95 per cent. of the product is to lie within specifications. We now read from the tables that 95 per cent. will lie within $\pm 1.96\sigma_1$ from the Mean, or

$$\text{Distance Spec. Mean-Tolerance} = 1.96\sigma_1,$$
and Distance Spec. Mean — 1/1000
$$\text{limit for 100 per cent. perfect product} = 1.96\frac{\sigma_1}{\sqrt{n}}.$$

Denoting that distance by D, and putting σ_1' for $\frac{\sigma_1}{\sqrt{n}}$, we have

$$D = 1.96\sigma_1'$$
$$\therefore \sigma_1' = .51\,D.$$

We then obtain our new control limits at $M \pm 3\sigma_1'$, or $M \pm 1.53\,D$.

In order to obtain control limits for other levels of defectiveness, we proceed in a completely analogous manner (see below, where the technique is condensed into eight brief rules).

If now the points within control limits are counted, and at the same time weighted according to whether they lie beyond the first (5% defectiveness) but within the second pair (10%) of control limits, beyond the second but within the third (15%) pair, and so forth, we obtain a number of "marks" for each chart. This figure is then deducted from the total number of points plotted on the chart, and the resulting figure divided by the total number. The ratio is called the *Quality Index*, and it is clear that it will be the smaller the greater the number of outliers and the farther away from the mean they occur. It should, however, be kept in mind that if the quality index is, say, 95 per cent., this does not mean that the product is 95 per cent. perfect. The method of marking introduces a strange element, with the result that the index figure is just as its name implies—an index, but not an exact description of quality.

Apart from forming the frame-work for the quality index, the pairs of control lines for different quality levels, if put into the margin of the chart, enable us to read at a glance the approximate level of defectiveness of our product by comparing these frame lines with the actually obtained limits in the body of the chart which is, perhaps, more important than the index figure.

(3) The technique for arriving at the control limits and the quality index figure can be condensed into the following 8 rules:

1. Obtain 1/1000 control limits for 100 per cent. perfect product from tolerances by dividing $(t_u - t_l)$ by $\sqrt{n}$ (n for sample size). Half the distance between these limits (D), measured on either side of the specification mean, represents three times the standard deviation of sample averages, σ', for perfect product.

2. Let $D = 1.96\sigma_1'$; $\sigma_1' = .51$ D. Then the specification mean $M \pm 3\sigma_1'$, or $M \pm 1.53$ D, gives the 1/1000 limits for averages of samples of n if the product is 5 per cent. defective (both sides taken together).

3. Let $D = 1.65\sigma_2'$; $\sigma_2' = .606$ D. Then the specification mean $M \pm 3\sigma_2'$, or $M = 1.82$ D, gives the 1/1000 limits for averages of samples of n if the product is 10 per cent. defective.

4. Let $D = 1.44\sigma_3'$; $\sigma_3' = .694$ D. Then the specification mean $M \pm 3\sigma_3'$, or $M = 2.08$ D, gives the 1/1000 limits for averages of samples of n if the product is 15 per cent. defective.

5. From the control limits based upon σ' (σ_1', σ_2', σ_3') it is possible to obtain the Average Range ($\bar{w}_n$) by dividing the quantities $3\sigma'$ ($3\sigma_1'$, $3\sigma_2'$, $3\sigma_3'$) by $A'._{001}$ (see Appendix IV). The control limits for the range are then obtained by multiplying $\bar{w}_n$ by the factors listed in Appendix IV.

6. The specification mean, together with the four pairs of 1/1000 limits for 0 per cent., 5 per cent., 10 per cent., 15 per cent. defective product obtained according to steps 1–4 for the chart of averages, and step 5 for the chart of ranges, are put into the *margin* of the respective chart which otherwise uses the control limits calculated from actual samples and recalculated from time to time.

At the end of the week (or the chart), the margin limits are prolonged in pencil over the whole length of the chart, and the points within and without limits are counted.

7. Treat the average and range chart for a given characteristic as one chart for the purpose of the quality index. Sum the points within the $3\sigma' - 3\sigma_1'$, $3\sigma_1' - 3\sigma_2'$, $3\sigma_2' - 3\sigma_3'$ bands on both charts, counting a sample which appears in a given band on both charts as one, and deduct for samples within

$$3\sigma' \text{ to } 3\sigma_1' \quad . \quad . \quad . \quad . \quad \text{. 1 point or 1 mark}$$
$$3\sigma_1' \text{ to } 3\sigma_2' \quad . \quad . \quad . \quad . \quad \text{. 2 points or 2 marks}$$
$$3\sigma_2' \text{ to } 3\sigma_3' \text{ or further} \quad . \quad \text{. 3 points or 3 marks}$$

Deduct from the total number of points the sum of all "marks," and divide by the total number of plotted points, that is, the number of sample averages. The quotient multiplied by 100 serves as the quality index.

8. For number defective charts, set a target at an acceptable limit of defectiveness (d). For a 5 per cent. increase in defectiveness find the 1/1000 limit for ($d + 5$) per cent. mean defectiveness (according to the sample size), and then proceed as with measurement charts (stages 6 and 7). Similarly for a 10 per cent. and 15 per cent. increase.

INDEX

Acceptance, probability of, 197, 198

Accidents, frequency distribution of, 139, 188 ; defectives as, 141 ; control lines for distribution of, 142 ; differing liability to, 188

Action on basis of control chart, 7, 26–31, 45, 64

Additive property of variances, 91

Ammunition, illustrative examples for controlling quality of, 26 sqq. ; and for inspection of, 178

Analysis of variance, principle of, 78 sqq. ; parallelism with quality control chart technique, 75 ; its use in testing significance of differences between means, 240, between standard deviations, 240, between percentages, 242 ; its relation to trends, 105 ; simplified methods of computation, 86, 89 ; multiple variate analysis, 99

Arithmetic mean, calculation of, 218 ; from arbitrary value, 219 ; standard error of, 21

Association, between two variables, 105 ; measure of, 119 ; see also Correlation

Asymmetrical or skew distributions, 69 sqq.

Attributes, see Sampling of attributes

Averages, of samples, 16 sqq. ; grand average, 22 ; distribution of standard deviation of, 21 ; control lines for, 22 ; factors for calculating control lines, 221 ; of range, 22 ; of standard deviation, 22 ; their importance for industrial control inspection, 43 ; see also under Mean

Bernoullian law, 173

" Best fit " of regression lines, 118, 135

Beta-function (also β-function), charts for incomplete β-function ratio, 225 sqq. ; tables, 228 sqq. ; instructions for using charts, 178 sqq.

Binomial distribution, 175 ; standard deviation of, 146 ; with negative index, 189n ; probability graphs of, 187, 190

Bivariate distributions, 109 ; intensity of dependence, 111 ; diagrammatic representation of, 114

Borderlines between stability and disturbance, 15

Bortkiewicz, L. von, data of death from kicks by a horse as Poisson distribution, 139

Brass discs, distribution of thickness of, 60 ; control chart for, 39

Brass shells, distribution of diameter, 70

Bravais, formula for correlation coefficient, 115 ; working formula, 115 ; illustration of working with Bravais's formula, 117

Bulk $v.$ sample quality, 171 sqq., 193 ; in the case of probability graphs, 53 sqq.

Camp-Meidell inequality, 68

Cartridges, assembling of, examples of control charts, 26 sqq.

Causes, assignable $v.$ chance, 26 ; probability of, 172 ; and effects, not in one-to-one correspondence, 173, 177

Cells in χ^2-test, of not less than five items, 56 ; comparison of frequencies, 241 ; see also under Chi-square

Chance, as complex causation, 4 ; of success or failure of an event, 175 ; laws of, 2 sqq.

Chances, small, as generating Poisson distribution, 140

Charts, see Control charts

Chi-square, 53 ; its relation to Poisson summation function, 57

Class interval, choice of magnitude of, 52 ; its influence on magnitude of standard deviation, 53

247

PRINTED IN GREAT BRITAIN AT
THE PRESS OF THE PUBLISHERS